CONTENTS

2010
Supplier Diversity Information Resource Guide

Eighteenth Edition

This is the sixteenth annual edition of the "Supplier Diversity Information Resource Guide". It is an easy-to-use comprehensive guide of diverse supplier business resources in the public and private sectors. Members of the Diversity Information Resources Board of Directors (listed, on the inside back cover), who assisted greatly in its publication, identified the need for this publication.

We invite your comments on this edition of the Supplier Diversity Information Resource Guide and welcome any recommendations for improvement.

Diversity Information Resources, Inc.
Leslie Bonds, Executive Director

NOTICE
The information in this publication was supplied by various individuals and agencies, and may be subject to change since the time of publication in December 2009. To check on the current status of any program, please call or write the appropriate contact listed.

Published annually by:

Diversity Information Resources, Inc. • 2105 Central Ave. N.E. • Minneapolis, MN 55418
Phone: (612) 781-6819 • Fax: (612) 781-0109
Web: www.diversityinforesources.com • Email: info@diversityinforesources.com

SECTION 1
LEGISLATION

The primary legislative initiatives which impact supplier diversity programs are listed in this section.

Public Law 95-507 (1978)
P.L. 95-507, passed in 1978, amended Section 8(d) of the Small Business Act and changed the way prime contractors and large businesses were to do business with the government. Prior to 1978, efforts to subcontract with small/small disadvantaged businesses were voluntary. They became mandatory with passage of P.L. 95-507, which stated that contracts over $10,000 must contain a "Utilization of Small Business Concerns and Small Business Concerns Owned and Controlled by Socially and Economically Disadvantaged Individuals" clause. For contracts over $500,000 ($1,000,000 for construction) P.L. 95-507 requires a subcontracting plan which sets percentage goals for utilizing small business concerns, including separate goals for disadvantaged small business. The prime contractor must describe what efforts it will make to ensure that SDBs have an equal opportunity to compete.

Note: Contract change to Public Law 95-507
Contracts over $550K ($1M construction) and subcontract opportunities exist. Modifications over $550K ($1M construction) with new work and subcontract opportunities exist. Multi-year contracts/contracts with options (cumulative value of base contract and all options, separate goals for base & each option).
Each subcontracting plan required under 19.702 must include separate percentage goals for using small business (including ANCs and Indian tribes), veteran-owned small business, service-disabled veteran-owned small business, HUBZone small business, small disadvantaged business (including ANCs and Indian tribes) and women-owned small business concerns as subcontractors.

More recent laws have further amended Section 8(d) of the Small Business Act, and additional goals have been added for women-owned small business (WOSB), HUBZone small business, Veteran-owned small business (VOSB), and Service-Disabled VOSB. The Small Business Act, including Section 8(d), is available on SBA's web site at www.sba.gov

Definitions used in P.L. 95-507 include:

I Small Business
- for manufactured products - size (employees)
- for service industries - annual sales

II Disadvantaged Small Business
- 51% owned and controlled by socially and economically disadvantaged individuals.

III Socially & Economically Disadvantaged
- Black Americans, Hispanic Americans, Native Americans (American Indians, Eskimos, Aleuts, and Native Hawaiians), Asian-Pacific Americans (U.S. citizens whose origins are from Burma, Thailand, Malaysia, Indonesia, Singapore, Brunei Japan, China, Taiwan, Laos, Cambodia, Kampuchea, Vietnam, Korea, the Philippines, Samoa, Guam, Macao, Hong Kong, Fiji, Tonga, Kiributi, Tuvalu, Nauru, US Trust Territories of the Pacific, Northern Marianas, Republic of Palau & Marshall Islands), and Subcontinent Asian Americans (U.S. citizens whose origins are from India, Pakistan, Bangladesh, Sri Lanka, Bhutan, the Maldives Islands or Nepal).
- Any individual found to be disadvantaged by SBA pursuant to section 8(a) of the Small Business Act.

IV Other individuals may qualify as socially and economically disadvantaged under procedures which have been established by SBA using the following guidelines:
- Socially disadvantaged individuals are those who have been subject to racial or ethnic prejudice or culture bias because of their identity as a group without regard to their individual qualities.

- Economically disadvantaged individuals are those socially disadvantaged individuals whose ability to compete in the free enterprise system has been impaired due to diminished capital and credit opportunities as compared to others in the same business area who are not socially disadvantaged. This law also contains provisions related to labor surplus areas, the small business set-aside program, preference goals, etc.

The law requires each federal agency with contracting authority to have an Office of Small and Disadvantaged Business Utilization (OSDBU). (See the list of OSDBU for locations/phone numbers.)

Public Law 97-219 - Small Business Innovation Research (SBIR) Program (1982)
The SBIR Program attempts to stimulate SB/SDB technological innovation. Under this program small, high-tech firms submit proposals for research projects in various research and development areas as outlined by individual federal agencies.

Public Law 99-661, Section 1207 (National Defense Authorization Act of 1987)
Establishes for DOD a three-year goal that 5% of procurement dollars go to small disadvantaged businesses (SDBs) and Historically Black Colleges and Universities (HBCUs), Minority Institutions (MI). Provisions include:

- "To the extent practicable," each contractor demonstrate full compliance with the intent of the law.
- Contractors may pay no more than fair market price (FMP), which may exceed 10% of the market price.
- Contractors may be criminally prosecuted for acts of misrepresentation.
- Contractors must report utilization for all separate groups that make up the protected class of minorities.

NOTE: This legislation subsequently was permanently codified (Section 2323 of Title 10, United States, Code) under Public Law 102-484.

Public Law 100-180, Section 806 (National Defense Authorization Act of 1988)
This legislation required that DOD maintain the level of contract awards/dollars for small business set-asides and 8(a) firms. It precludes the use of SDB set-asides when the requirement was previously acquired under small business set-asides or 8(a).

S. 2941, which is part of Public Law 102-564, The Small Business R&D Enhancement Act of 1992
This legislation reauthorizes the Small Business Innovation Research Program (SBIR) and increases the percentage of federal research funds which are set aside for small businesses. From a current 1.25% dedication of funds for innovative research projects, the statute calls for not less than 2% in FY 95-96 and 2.5% in FY 97 and years following. (For more information, contact one of the Federal agency SBIR programs).

Public Law 100-442 (Amending Indian Financing Act of 1974)
Authorizes payment of a 5% incentive of the subcontract to prime contractors for subcontracting with Native American firms.

Public Law 100-533 - Women's Business Ownership Act of 1988
Four primary areas covered in this legislation are:

- Demonstration projects up to $10 million over a 3-year period to fund marketing, financial, and management assistance to WBEs.
- Access to capital (incentive for SBA Certified Loan Program lenders)
- Creates National Women's Business Council
- Calls for compilation of statistical data.

Public Law 100-590, Section 110 (SBA Reauthorization and Amendment Act of 1988)
Revises several aspects of the 8(a) program, including Section 129, Rural Area Business Development Plan, which requires federal agencies to develop rural enterprise plans to increase prime/subcontract awards to small businesses in rural areas.

Public Law 100-656 Business Opportunity Development Act of 1988.
A complex piece of legislation which (1) revised aspects of the 8(a) program; (2) authorized assessment of

liquidated damages against prime contractor that fails to make a good-faith effort to meet its contracting goals, including its SDB goal; and (3) established a test program suspending small business set-asides in four industry groups (construction, refuse collection, architectural engineering and non-nuclear ship repair.)

Other measures included in 100-656:

- Increased 8(a) participation from maximum of 7 to 9 years.
- Established two stages to 8(a) program: developmental to last no more than four years and transitional to last no longer than five years.
- Shifted business plan requirements for participants.
- Reorganized termination and graduation standards.
- Increased penalties for misrepresentation in the 8(a) program, with potential fines of up to $500,000 and/or ten years in prison.
- Required contracts of more than $5 million (manufacturing) and over $3 million (all other types) to be awarded on the basis of competition restricted to eligible program participants.
- Established a government-wide goal for SDB participation of not less than 5% of the total value of all prime contracts and subcontract awards for each fiscal year.

Public Law 101-144 and 101-507

Mandates that NASA achieve an annual goal of awarding 8% of its contracting dollars to SDBs by the close of FY 94. The legislation allows small woman-owned firms to be counted in the 8% goal. According to NASA FAR Supplement 18-19.7001, the 8% can be flowed down to prime contractors and NASA will receive credit for subcontract awards made by primes and SDBs.

Public Law 101-189 (National Defense Authorization Act of 1990)

Sections of this legislation include:

- Extension of 5% goal for SDBs through 1993. (The 5% goal is now permanent).
- Requirement that DOD establish procedures to adjust price preference evaluations for SDBs tailored by industry category in categories where the SDB is being denied a reasonable opportunity to participate.
- Sets up procedural requirements re subcontract goal accreditation for work by American Indian firms on reservations.
- Requires DOD to identify and award 30 construction contracts in FY 1990 and 1991 to minority owned firms with the surety bond prerequisite waived.
- Requires each military department to select a large prime contractor, negotiate and monitor with them a large comprehensive test subcontracting plan (single plan for aggregate contracts rather than multiple plans for each individual contract).

Public Law 101-510 (National Defense Authorization Act of 1991)

Legislation affects several sections of the National Defense Authorization Act and establishes the Mentor-Protege Program (see Mentor Protege Program for detailed description). Affected sections of this statute include:

- Establishment of a $25,000 small purchase threshold which will be adjusted for inflation every five years.
- DOD pilot program under which certain [subcontracting] provisions of the law may be waived.
- Clarifies eligibility of SDB advertising firms.
- Requires DOD contractors to obtain disclosures from their subcontractors at the time of award as to whether they have been debarred or suspended.

Mentor Protege Program (Section 831)

Defense contractors act as mentors to SDB proteges by providing training and technical assistance. Mentors may have more than one protege, but proteges are limited to one mentor. A Protege must be either an SDB or a qualified organization employing the disabled. Mentors will be eligible for reimbursement from the federal government. Some of the contractor's costs can be applied toward the 5% goal. Prospective mentor companies apply to DOD for program participation.

Under terms of the Program, mentors may:

- award noncompetitive contracts to their proteges.
- provide loans or invest in ownership of protege companies not to exceed 10%.
- make progress payments of up to 100% of cost incurred.

Prime contractors (mentors) may credit the cost of developing the capability of the SDB (protege) toward the SDB contracting goal, or receive reimbursement for these costs, or a combination of both. Mentors and proteges enter into an agreement (approved by DOD) indicating the types of assistance to be provided, assessment factors, and anticipated subcontracts that will be awarded. Once approved, mentors can award noncompetitive, sole source subcontracts to the protege. There are three options for reimbursing mentors for costs of developing proteges:

- contract line item added to existing DOD contract;
- separate contract, or other agreement with DOD;
- through costs allocated to an indirect expense pool.

NOTE: The above is only a brief outline of the program. For complete information, obtain a copy of the Defense Federal Acquisition Regulations (DFAR) and the Department of Defense policy on the Mentor Protege Program.

Public Law 102-486 Comprehensive National Energy Policy Act

Requires not less than 10% of federal contracts and subcontracts awarded for energy conservation in government buildings, purchase of natural gas-powered vehicles and energy research and development be awarded to minority and women-owned businesses.

Public Law 103-355 Federal Acquisition Streamlining Act

Major provisions include:

- 5% government-wide contracting goal for small disadvantaged businesses. Authorize set-asides or 10% price preference on unrestricted competition.
- 5% contracting goal for all federal agencies with women-owned businesses.
- Small business set-aside threshold raised from $25,000 to $100,000.
- Sets up government electronic procurement system (FACNET) which will be implemented by January 1, 2000.
- Encourage purchase of commercial products up to $50,000 (up to $100,000 for agencies implementing FACNET).
- Establishes a micropurchase level of $2,500 under which purchasers can buy products under $2,500 from any source; encouraged to use government credit cards.

Adarand vs. Pena

In a 5 to 4 decision, the U.S. Supreme Court ruled in 1995 that preferential treatment based on race must meet the legal standard known as "strict scrutiny," which means that (1) there must be a compelling Government interest; and (2) the remedy must be narrowly tailored to address the injury. Since no one disputes that there is a compelling Government interest in such matters, the requirement for narrow tailoring is the critical issue. Narrow tailoring requires disparity studies, usually by industry and sometimes geographically as well, showing the industries or regions where minority-owned firms are underrepresented, indicating continuing discrimination or the ongoing effects of past discrimination.

The decision does not ban set-aside programs outright, but it does mean that each set-aside program must be able to prove that it is based on a specific case of past discrimination.

The Supreme Court turned the Adarand case back to the lower court, and the lower court must now use the "strict scrutiny" standard to decide whether the Department of Transportation's subcontracting program will stand.

NOTE: This case has had major impact on all race and gender-based programs. Several cases have been heard in the lower courts, with most decisions favoring those challenging race-based purchasing programs. The Department of Justice was asked to develop a Rule which would address discrimination in various industries.

Public Law 104-106, Federal Acquisition Reform Act of 1996 - included in 1996 Department of Defense Authorization Bill

This bill holds major impact on federal procurement, as its provisions cover all federal agencies. Commonly known as "FARA" or the "Clinger-Cohen Act," its key features are:

- Simplifies procedures for buying commercial items up to a threshold of $5 million;
- Eliminates some government-unique terms and conditions for the purchase of commercial off-the-shelf items;
- Permits government contracting officers to use two-phase competition on certain construction contracts;
- Reduces litigation on information technology purchases, as bid protest hearings are consolidated at GAO.
- Redirects information technology procurement into the normal budgeting process (eliminates GSA approval requirements).

NOTE: Regulations governing the above will now be formulated, and much of the bill's impact on small/minority businesses will depend on the wording of the regulations. Of particular concern to small/minority business is the bill's allowing agencies to bypass the full and open competition standard when it is not deemed "feasible or appropriate."

Public Law 106-50 – Veterans Business Outreach Program (VBOP)
Authorized by section 708 of the Small Business Reauthorization Act of 1997. VBOP is one of SBA's new initiatives to expand outreach to veterans. Through VBOP, SBA awarded grants to set up four Veteran's Business Outreach Centers (VBOCs) in different regions to provide business training, counseling, technical assistance, and mentorship to service-disabled veterans.

Under the Veterans Entrepreneurship and Small Business Development Act of 1999, enacted on August 16, 1999 (Public Law 106-50), SBA also plans to enter into agreements with the Service Corps of Retired Executives (SCORE) and the Small Business Development Centers (SBDCs), to further enhance delivery of technical assistance and business training to veterans, including service-disabled veterans.

Under this new legislation, the SBA will develop distance-learning tools and training for veterans and conduct studies on veteran-owned small businesses. The SBA currently is designing online classrooms tailored to the entrepreneurial needs of veterans as part of the agency's small business classroom distance learning initiative at www.sba.gov/training/

The agency will also assist veterans in finding procurement opportunities with federal, state, and local agencies. Veteran-owned small businesses currently could register in PRO-Net, SBA's procurement database. PRO-Net provides a search engine that allows federal contracting officers and prime contractors to search for veteran-owned small businesses. Public Law 106-50 mandates a 3 percent federal procurement goal for service-disabled veteran-owned small businesses.

Public Law 109-461 (Veterans Benefits, Health Care, and Information Technology Act of 2006)
Signed into law by President Bush on December 22, 2006. This law provides VA with unique authority to conduct set-aside and sole source procurements with small businesses owned and operated by veterans.

Executive Order 13360, Contracting with Service-Disabled Veterans' Businesses
On October 20th, 2004, the President signed Executive Order 13360 calling for an increase federal contracting and subcontracting opportunities for service-disabled veteran businesses. On December 12th, 2004, the Executive Office of the President issued a memorandum to all Federal agencies on the implementation of the Executive Order. This memorandum provides guidance to assist agencies in preparing their strategies to implement the Order.

Among other things, the Order requires each agency to:

1. develop a strategy to significantly increase its contracting and subcontracting with small businesses owned and controlled by service-disabled veterans;

2. designate a senior-level official to be responsible for developing and implementing the agency's strategy; and

3. report its progress annually to the Small Business Administration (SBA).

California's Proposition 209
On November 5, 1996, California voters passed Proposition 209. It prohibits state and local government bodies from granting preferential treatment to any individual or group on the basis of race, sex, color, ethnicity or national origin in areas of public hiring, contracting or education. The initiative has no effect on affirmative action programs run by the federal government or private businesses and colleges.

The Supreme's Court decision to let a lower court ruling stand means opponents of the measure are out of legal options. Thus, Proposition 209 will not be challenged in the foreseeable future. Supporters of 209 have begun to sue cities and counties for maintaining affirmative-action programs that may violate the new law. Any of these suits could end up before the U.S. Supreme Court, giving the justices another chance to review Proposition 209.

Proposition 200 — State of Washington
Proposition 200 was passed November 1998. It uses the same language as Proposition 209.

HUBZones — Historically Underutilized Business Zones www.sba.gov/hubzone/ (See Section 10)
The Small Business Reauthorization Act addresses the issue of economically distressed urban and rural areas:
- To be eligible a business must be small, must be located in a designated HUBZone, and must hire not less than 35% of its workforce from the HUBZone.
- Allow prices and non-price incentives, including a 10% price preference on competitive awards.
- Provide for sole-source awards on manufacturing contracts under $5 million ($3 million of all types of contracts).
- Provide equal consideration to HUBZone eligible firms as that of 8(a) firms in the procurement hierarchy.

Contract Bundling
On March 19, 2002, the President unveiled a Small Business Agenda that proposed several substantive steps toward creating a dynamic environment where small businesses and entrepreneurs can flourish. The plan included new tax incentives, health care options, and a reduction in regulatory barriers. And for those small businesses seeking to do business with the federal government, the President announced several proposals to improve the access of small businesses to federal contracting opportunities. Specifically, the President called upon the Office of Management and Budget (OMB) to prepare a strategy for unbundling contracts.

Definition
Small Business Reauthorization Act of 1997 defines contract bundling as "consolidating two or more procurement requirements for goods or services previously provided or performed under separate, smaller contracts into a solicitation of offers for a single contract that is unlikely to be suitable for award to a small business concern." The Act lists several factors that might cause unsuitability for award to a small business. These are:
- The diversity, size, or specialized nature of the elements of the performance specified;
- the aggregate dollar value of the anticipated award;
- the geographical dispersion of contract performance sites; or
- any combination of these criteria.

The Act requires each federal department and agency, to the maximum extent practicable, to: (1) structure contracting requirements to facilitate competition by and among small business concerns, taking all reasonable steps to eliminate obstacles to their participation; and (2) avoid unnecessary and unjustified bundling of contract requirements that may preclude small business participation in procurements as prime contractors.

Prior to bundling any contracts, agencies are required to conduct market research to determine whether contract bundling is necessary and justified. To justify contract bundling, agencies must demonstrate "measurably substantial benefits," such as cost savings, quality improvements, reduction in acquisition cycle times, or better terms and conditions.2 The Small Business Administration's implementing regulations further define "measurably substantial benefits" by requiring agencies to demonstrate:
- For contracts of $75 million or less - - benefits equivalent to 10 percent of contract value (including options), or
- for contracts over $75 million - - benefits equivalent to 5 percent of contract value (including options) or $7.5 million, whichever is greater.

Several provisions of the Federal Acquisition Regulation (FAR) establish responsibilities for agency personnel who are considering contract bundling. The FAR places responsibility on agency acquisition planners to structure requirements, to the maximum extent practicable, to facilitate competition by and among small business concerns, and avoid unnecessary and unjustified bundling. Agency contracting officers are required to: (1) perform market research to determine whether bundling is necessary and justified; (2) justify their determinations in acquisition strategy documentation that identifies measurably substantial benefits that meet the statutory and regulatory requirements; and (3) consult with SBA representatives on their acquisition strategies.

Why Are Contracts Bundled?

Increased demands to make the acquisition process quicker and less complex coupled with reductions in the overall acquisition workforce have driven acquisition managers to bundle requirements. To meet these demands and increase customer satisfaction, agencies have increasingly consolidated contractual requirements into larger contracts and used limited and simplified competition procedures for acquiring products and services.

What is the Impact of Contract Bundling on Small Businesses?

According to a report prepared for SBA's Office of Advocacy, for every 100 "bundled" contracts, 106 individual contracts are no longer available to small businesses. For every $100 awarded on a "bundled" contract, there is a $33 decrease to small businesses. Because these types of contracts "run longer and encompass a greater scope, competition is reduced in terms of frequency and the number of opportunities." Analysis of the data indicates that, even though the overall dollars spent in contracting with small businesses remained relatively constant, there has been a sharp overall decline in new contract awards. Figure 1 shows a decline in new contract awards (i.e., new contracts rather than contract modifications or orders under existing contracts), from a high of 86,243 in fiscal year 1991 to a low of 34,261 in fiscal year 2001.

SECTION 2

SMALL BUSINESS ADMINISTRATION

US Small Business Administration (SBA)
409 Third Street, SW
Washington, DC 20416
1-800-U-ASK-SBA (1-800-827-5722)
www.sba.gov

The U.S. Small Business Administration (SBA) was created in 1953 as an independent agency of the federal government to aid, counsel, assist and protect the interests of small business concerns, to preserve free competitive enterprise and to maintain and strengthen the overall economy of our nation. We recognize that small business is critical to our economic recovery and strength, to building America's future, and to helping the United States compete in today's global marketplace. Although SBA has grown and evolved in the years since it was established in 1953, the bottom line mission remains the same. The SBA helps Americans start, build and grow businesses. Through an extensive network of field offices and partnerships with public and private organizations, SBA delivers its services to people throughout the United States, Puerto Rico, the U. S. Virgin Islands and Guam.

8(a) Business Development Program
The 8(a) Program (named for Section 8(a) of the Small Business Act) is a business development program created to help small disadvantaged businesses compete in the market place. It is also designed to assist such companies in gaining access to federal and private procurement markets.

The focus of the program is to provide business development support, such as mentoring, procurement assistance, business counseling, training, financial assistance, surety bonding and other management and technical assistance. The goal, however, is to prepare small disadvantaged firms for procurement and other business opportunities.

Central Contractor Registration (CCR) – www.ccr.gov
CCR is the primary registrant database for the U.S. Federal Government. CCR collects, validates, stores, and disseminates data in support of agency acquisition missions, including Federal agency contract and assistance awards. Please note that the term "assistance awards" includes grants, cooperative agreements and other forms of federal assistance. Whether applying for assistance awards, contracts, or other business opportunities, all entities are considered "registrants".

Both current and potential federal government registrants are required to register in CCR in order to be awarded contracts by the federal government. Registrants are required to complete a one-time registration to provide basic information relevant to procurement and financial transactions. Registrants must update or renew their registration at least once per year to maintain an active status. In addition, entities (private non-profits, educational organizations, state and regional agencies, etc.) that apply for assistance awards from the Federal Government through Grants.gov must now register with CCR as well. However, registration in no way guarantees that a contract or assistance award will be awarded.

CCR validates the registrant information and electronically shares the secure and encrypted data with the federal agencies' finance offices to facilitate paperless payments through electronic funds transfer (EFT). Additionally, CCR shares the data with federal government procurement and electronic business systems.

Small Disadvantaged Business (SDB) Self-Certification

As of Oct. 3, 2008 companies seeking to obtain federal prime or subcontracts can self-certify their status as small disadvantaged businesses (an option that has been available since 2004) or use a third-party private certification firm. In limited circumstances, the procuring agency can certify the company. Companies already certified as small disadvantaged or 8(a) firms will not be affected until that status is scheduled for renewal.

Note: Effective October 3, 2008

The Small Business Administration will no longer verify the status of companies seeking certification as small disadvantaged businesses, shifting the time-consuming and costly application process to the companies themselves or to third parties.In an interim final rule published in the *Federal Register*, SBA explained that the value of the small disadvantaged business designation has tailed off in recent years as the financial incentives have disappeared or been ignored. This rule changes the requirements relating to which firms may certify their status as small disadvantaged businesses (SDBs) for purposes of federal prime contracts and subcontracts. Currently, only those firms that have applied to and been certified as SDBs by SBA may certify themselves to be SDBs for federal prime and subcontracts. This rule allows firms to self-represent their status for subcontracting purposes without first receiving any SDB certification. It also recognizes that the benefits of being an SDB for federal prime contracts has been greatly diminished over the past years, and shifts the responsibility of identifying firms as SDBs for federal prime contracts to those limited agencies that have authority and chose to use price evaluation adjustments to SDBs.

Evaluation Factor and Monetary Incentive for Subcontracting with Small Disadvantaged Businesses

Federal Acquisition Regulations (FAR) subpart 19.12, Small Disadvantaged Business Participation Program, is applicable to all solicitations issued on or after January 1, 1999. This rule creates a source selection evaluation factor or subfactor for planned SDB participation in the performance of a contract in the NAICS sub sectors (formerly SIC major groups), as well as a mechanism to evaluate past performance of contractors in complying with their SDB participation targets. It also creates a monetary incentive for subcontracting with SDBs. For more information on the list of authorized industries see http://www.acquisition.gov/references/sdbadjustments.htm

North American Industry Classification System (NAICS)

On October 1, 2000, the SBA began using the North American Industry Classification System (NAICS) in place of the Standard Industry Classifications, or SIC codes, which had been the method of categorizing businesses for almost 60 years. NAICS were developed in the early 1990s as a result of the North American Free Trade Act. Each number identifies an industry or sub sector of an industry. Canada, Mexico, and the US have all agreed to use the same codes and definitions to track trade flow between the three countries more accurately.

The SBA assigns subcategories for each code based on revenue and number of employees. The SBA uses them to determine which small businesses in each sector qualify for its guaranteed loans and preference programs in bidding on federal contracts. Under the NAICS new classifications, a few companies will be considered too large to qualify for the agency's programs and others will have to compete against larger companies for federal contracts.

The programs that will be most affected by code changes are the ones that give disadvantaged businesses an assist in bidding for federal contracts, including the section 8(a) program, which reserves a certain number of government contracts specifically for minority-owned businesses. The SBA says companies that apply for these are likely to be affected more than those applying for loans, because companies of varying sizes compete for government contracts whereas only the smallest companies tend to apply for SBA loans.

Business Size Determination Guidelines

To determine whether a company is a large or small business use the North American Industry Classification System (NAICS) code at www.census.gov/epcd/naics02/naico602.htm. After determining the NAICS code, refer to the industry size standards published by the Small Business Administration at www.sba.gov/size/sizetable2002.html to determine whether a company is classified as a large or a small business under that NAICS code. For additional information on determining business size, please refer to the SBA Guide to Definitions of Small Business at www.sba.gov/size/indexguide.html

Business Classification Definitions

Veteran-Owned Small Business

"Veteran-Owned Small Business" as used in this provision means a small business that: is at least 51% unconditionally owned by one or more veterans (as defined at 38 U.S.C. 101(2)); or in the case of any publicly owned business, at least 51% of the stock of which is unconditionally owned by one or more veterans; and whose management and daily business operations are controlled by one or more veterans.

Service-Disabled Veteran-Owned Small Business

"Service-Disabled Veteran-Owned Small Business" as used in this provision means a small business that: is at least 51% unconditionally owned by one or more service-disabled veterans (as defined at 38 U.S.C. 101(2), with a disability that is service connected, as defined in 38 U.S.C. 101(16)); or in the case of any publicly owned business, at least 51% of the stock of which is unconditionally owned by one or more service-disabled veterans; and whose management and daily business operations are controlled by one or more service-disabled veterans or, in the case of a veteran with permanent and severe disability, the spouse or permanent caregiver of such veteran.

HUBZone Small Business

"HUBZone Small Business" as used in this provision means a small business that appears on the list of Qualified HUBZone Small Business maintained by the US Small Business Administration
https://eweb1.sba.gov/hubzone/internet/

Socially and Economically Disadvantaged Individuals

Socially disadvantaged individuals are those who have been subjected to racial or ethnic prejudice or cultural bias because of their identities as members of groups without regard to their individual qualities. The social disadvantage must stem from circumstances beyond their control.

In the absence of evidence to the contrary, the following individuals are presumed to be socially disadvantaged:

- Black Americans;
- Hispanic Americans (persons with origins from Latin America, South America, Portugal and Spain);
- Native Americans (American Indians, Eskimos, Aleuts, and Native Hawaiians);
- Asian Pacific Americans (persons with origins from Japan, China, the Philippines, Vietnam, Korea, Samoa, Guam, U.S. Trust Territory of the Pacific Islands [Republic of Palau], Commonwealth of the Northern Mariana Islands, Laos, Cambodia [Kampuchea], Taiwan, Burma, Thailand, Malaysia, Indonesia, Singapore, Brunei, Republic of the Marshall Islands, Federated States of Micronesia, Macao, Hong Kong, Fiji, Tonga, Kiribati, Tuvalu, or Nauru);
- Subcontinent Asian Americans (persons with origins from India, Pakistan, Bangladesh, Sri Lanka, Bhutan, the Maldives Islands or Nepal).

Economically disadvantaged individuals are socially disadvantaged individuals whose ability to compete in the free enterprise system has been impaired due to diminished capital and credit opportunities, as compared to othersin the same or similar line of business and competitive market area who are not socially disadvantaged. For purposes of program entry, an individual whose personal net worth (excluding the equity in their personal residence and business) exceeds $250,000 will not be considered economically disadvantaged.

Woman-Owned Business

A woman-owned business may be recognized as a "socially disadvantaged firm" if the owner is a member of one of the groups for which social disadvantage is presumed. If the woman is not a member of one of the groups for which social disadvantage is presumed, she must establish her individual disadvantage on the basis of clear and convincing evidence that she has suffered discriminatory treatment because of her gender and that this treatment has impeded her entry into or advancement in the business world. SBA will consider any pertinent evidence but will give particular attention to evidence of discriminatory practices suffered in the areas of education, employment and the business world.

Small Business

SBA defines a small business as one that is independently owned and operated and is not dominant in its field. Depending on the industry, size standard eligibility is based on the average number of employees for the preceding 12-months or on sales volume averaged over a three-year period. Examples of SBA general size standards include the following:

Manufacturing: Maximum number of employees may range from 500 to 1500, depending on the type of product manufactured.

Wholesale: Maximum number of employees may not exceed 100.

Services: Annual receipts may not exceed $2.5 to $21.5 million, depending on the particular service being provided.

Retail: Annual receipts may not exceed $5.0 to $21.0 million, depending on the particular product being provided.

General & Heavy Construction: General construction annual receipts may not exceed $13.5 to $17 million, depending on the type of construction.

Special Trade Construction: Annual receipts may not exceed $7 million.

Agriculture: Annual receipts may not exceed $0.5 to $5.0 million, depending on the agricultural product.

Years in Business

You normally have to be in business for two years in order to be eligible for the 8(a) program. However, a waiver of the two-year rule may be granted if a company meets certain criteria. The waiver criteria are:

A. the individual(s) upon whom eligibility is to be based must have substantial and demonstrated business management experience;
B. the applicant must have demonstrated technical expertise to carry out its business plan with a substantial likelihood for success;
C. the applicant must have adequate capital to carry out its business plan;
D. the applicant must have a record of successful performance on contracts from governmental and non-governmental sources in the primary industry category in which the applicant is seeking program certification; and
E. the applicant must have or be able to demonstrate the ability to obtain the personnel, facilities, equipment and any other requirements needed to perform the contract.

SBA PROGRAMS

7(j) Management and Technical Assistance Program
Under Section 7(j) of the Small Business Act, the MED office enters into contracts, grants and cooperative agreements with service providers to provide targeted assistance in accounting, marketing and proposal/bid preparation. Industry-specific technical assistance and entrepreneurial training also are available. (The SBA does not provide grants to start or expand businesses.)

Targeted customers are small disadvantaged businesses, low-income individuals, firms in either labor-surplus areas or areas with a high proportion of low-income individuals.

The program is delivered through 7(j) providers of management and technical assistance, (including small business concerns, minority educational institutions, and other educational institutions), SBA.

Government Contracting

- Certificate of Competency - helps small businesses receive government contracts by providing appeal process to low bidder denied contracts.
- Prime Contract - increases small business opportunities in federal acquisition process through set-asides, counseling, compliance assessment, etc.
- Breakout Program - promotes breakout of historically sole-source items for full and open competition.
- Subcontracting - ensures that small business receives maximum opportunity to participate in federal contracts as subcontractors and suppliers.

US Export Assistance Centers
One-stop shops combine the trade promotion and export finance resources of the SBA, the U.S. Department of Commerce and the Export-Import Bank. SBATLAS - provides key market data to exporters.

Export Legal Assistance Network (ELAN)
Provides initial free legal consultations to small business exporters. Experienced trade attorneys volunteer their time to answer exporters' legal questions.

Business Information Centers (BICs)
BIC's provide the latest in high-tech hardware, software and telecommunications to help small businesses get started and grow. Counseling and training are provided by SCORE.

Veterans Affairs
Business management and technical training, counseling, technology transfer conferences.

Small Business Development Centers (SBDCs)
Provides management and technical assistance to current and prospective small business owners (see list of SBDC's in this section).

Small Business Innovation Research (SBIR) Program
Provides opportunities for small, innovative companies to compete in federally funded research and development. (See list of SBIR's in this section).

Service Corps of Retired Executives (SCORE)
12,400 member volunteer program which matches volunteers with small businesses needing expert advise. Contact local SBA district office (See list of SBA district offices in this section).

Native American Affairs
Stimulate interaction, communication, coordination and delivery of SBA programs to Native American businesses.

FINANCE, INVESTMENT AND PROCUREMENT PROGRAMS

Basic 7(a) Loan Guaranty

Serves as the SBA's primary business loan program to help qualified small businesses obtain financing when they might not be eligible for business loans through normal lending channels. It is also the agency's most flexible business loan program, since financing under this program can be guaranteed for a variety of general business purposes.

Loan proceeds can be used for most sound business purposes including working capital, machinery and equipment, furniture and fixtures, land and building (including purchase, renovation and new construction), leasehold improve ments, and debt refinancing (under special conditions). Loan maturity is up to 10 years for working capital and generally up to 25 years for fixed assets. SBA offers multiple variations of the basic 7(a) loan program to accommodate targeted needs.

CUSTOMER: Start-up and existing small businesses, commercial lending institutions

DELIVERED THROUGH: Commercial lending institutions

www.sba.gov/financing/sbaloan/7a.html

Certified Development Company (CDC), a 504 Loan Program

Provides long-term, fixed-rate financing to small businesses to acquire real estate or machinery or equipment for expansion or modernization. Typically a 504 project includes a loan secured from a private-sector lender with a senior lien, a loan secured from a CDC (funded by a 100 percent SBA-guaranteed debenture) with a junior lien covering up to 40 percent of the total cost, and a contribution of at least 10 percent equity from the borrower.

CUSTOMER: Small businesses requiring "brick and mortar" financing

DELIVERED THROUGH: Certified development companies (private, nonprofit corporations set up to contribute to the economic development of their communities or regions)

www.sba.gov/financing/sbaloan/cdc504.html

Microloan, a 7(m) Loan Program

Provides short-term loans of up to $35,000 to small businesses and not-for-profit child-care centers for working capital or the purchase of inventory, supplies, furniture, fixtures, machinery and/or equipment. Proceeds cannot be used to pay existing debts or to purchase real estate. The SBA makes or guarantees a loan to an intermediary, who in turn, makes the microloan to the applicant. These organizations also provide management and technical assistance. The SBA does not guarantee the loans. The microloan program is available in selected locations in most states.

CUSTOMER: Small businesses and not-for-profit child-care centers needing small-scale financing and technical assistance for start-up or expansion

DELIVERED THROUGH: Specially designated intermediary lenders (nonprofit organizations with experience in lending and in technical assistance)

www.sba.gov/financing/sbaloan/microloans.html

Loan Prequalification

Allows a business applicant to have their loan applications for $250,000 or less analyzed and potentially sanctioned by the SBA before they are taken to lenders for consideration. The program focuses on the applicant's character, credit, experience and reliability rather than assets. An SBA-designated intermediary works with the business owner to review and strengthen the loan application. The review is based on key financial ratios, credit and business history, and the loan-request terms. The SBA's Office of Field Operations and SBA district offices administer the program.

CUSTOMER: Designated small businesses

DELIVERED THROUGH: Intermediaries operating in specific geographic areas

www.sba.gov/financing/sbaloan/prequalification.html

Export Working Capital

The Export Working Capital Program (EWCP) was designed to provide short-term working capital to exporters. The SBA's Export Working Capital Program (EWCP) supports export financing to small businesses when that financing is not otherwise available on reasonable terms. The program encourages lenders to offer export working capital loans by guaranteeing repayment of up to $1.5 million or 90 percent of a loan amount, whichever is less. A loan can support a single transaction or multiple sales on a revolving basis.

Designed to provide short-term working capital to exporters, the EWCP is a combined effort of the SBA and the Export-Import Bank. The two agencies have joined their working capital programs to offer a unified approach to the government's support of export financing. The EWCP uses a one-page application form and streamlined documentation with turnaround usually 10 days or less. A letter of prequalification is also available from the SBA.

Export Working Capital Program Eligibility (EWCP)

In addition to the eligibility standards listed below, an applicant must be in business for a full year (not necessarily in exporting) at the time of application. SBA may waive this requirement if the applicant has sufficient export trade experience. Export management companies or export trading companies my use this program; however, title must be taken in the goods being exported to be eligible.

Most small businesses are eligible for SBA loans; some types of businesses are ineligible and a case-by-case determination must be made by the Agency. Eligibility is generally determined Business Type, Use of Proceeds, Size of Business, and Availability of Funds from other sources. The following links provide more detailed information about each of these areas.

The proceeds of an EWCP loan must be used to finance the working capital needs associated with a single or multiple transactions of the exporter.

Proceeds may not be used to finance professional export marketing advice or services, foreign business travel, participating in trade shows or U.S. support staff in overseas, except to the extent it relates directly to the transaction being financed. In addition, "proceeds may not be used" to make payments to owners, to pay delinquent withholding taxes, or to pay existing debt.

The applicant must establish that the loan will significantly expand or develop an export market, is currently adversely affected by import competition, will upgrade equipment or facilities to improve competitive position, or must be able to provide a business plan that reasonably projects export sales sufficient to cover the loan.

Export Working Capital Program (EWCP) Maturities

SBA guarantees the short-term working capital loans made by participating Lenders to exporters. An export loan can be for a single or multiple transactions. If the loan is for a single transaction, the maturity should correspond to the length of the transaction cycle with a maximum maturity of 18 months. If the loan is for a revolving line of credit, the maturity is typically twelve (12) months, with annual re-issuances allowed two times, for a maximum maturity of three years.

www.sba.gov/financing/loanprog/ewcp.html

Export Express

SBA Export Express combines the SBA's small business lending assistance with its technical assistance programs to help small businesses that have traditionally had difficulty in obtaining adequate export financing. The pilot program is available throughout the country and is expected to run through September 30, 2005.

SBA Export Express helps small businesses that have exporting potential, but need funds to buy or produce goods, and/or to provide services, for export. Loan proceeds may be used to finance export development activities such as:

- Participation in a foreign trade show;
- Translation of product brochures or catalogues for use in overseas markets;
- General lines of credit for export purposes;
- Service contracts from buyers located outside the United States;
- Transaction-specific financing needs associated with completing actual export orders; and/or
- Purchase of real estate and equipment to be used in production of goods or services which will be expansion,
- Provide term loans and other financing to enable small business concerns, including export trading companies and export management companies, to develop foreign markets; and
- Acquire, construct, renovate, modernize, improve or expand productive facilities or equipment to be used in the United States in the production of goods or services involved in international trade.

Who Can Use this Program?

SBA Export Express loans are available to persons who meet the normal requirements for an SBA business loan guaranty. Loan applicants must also:

- demonstrate that the loan proceeds will enable them to enter a new export market or expand an existing export market, and
- have been in business operation, though not necessarily in exporting, for at least 12 months.

Technical Assistance

Because many small business exporters face unique problems and challenges, the SBA Export Express Program also includes technical assistance in the form of marketing, management and planning assistance.

SBA's US Export Assistance Centers, in cooperation with SBA's network of resource partners, including the Small Business Development Centers (SBDCs) and Service Corps of Retired Executives (SCORE) provide technical assistance.

On approval of an SBA Export Express loan, a U.S. Export Assistance Center representative will contact the borrower to offer appropriate assistance. This assistance may include training offered through the SBA's Export Trade Assistance Partnership, SBDC International Trade Center, SCORE, District Export Council, or Export Legal Assistance Network.

www.sba.gov/financing/loanprog/exportexpress.html

International Trade Loans

If your business is preparing to engage in or is already engaged in international trade, or is adversely affected by competition from imports, the International Trade Loan Program is designed for you.

International Trade Loan Eligibility

The applicant must establish that the loan will significantly expand or develop an export market, is currently adversely affected by import competition, will upgrade equipment or facilities to improve competitive position, or must be able to provide a business plan that reasonably projects export sales sufficient to cover the loan.

Although most small businesses are eligible for SBA loans, some types of businesses are ineligible and a case-by-case determination must be made by the Agency.

The proceeds of a SBA International Trade loan may be used to acquire, construct, renovate, modernize, improve or expand facilities and equipment to be used in the United States to produce goods or services involved in international trade; or the refinancing of existing indebtedness that is not structured with reasonable terms and conditions. There can be no working capital as part of an IT loan or as part of any refinancing.

A small business concern is engaged in international trade if, as determined by SBA, "the small business concern is in a position to expand existing export markets or develop new export markets."

A small business concern is adversely affected by international trade if, as determined by SBA, "the small business concern (i) is confronting increased competition with foreign firms in the relevant market; and (ii) is injured by such competition."

Loans for facilities or equipment can have maturities of up to 25 years.

The maximum gross amount ($2 million) and SBA-guaranteed amount ($1.5 million) for an IT loan is the same as a regular 7(a) loan. However, there is an exception to the maximum SBA 7(a) guaranty amount to one borrower (including affiliates).

The maximum guaranteed amount can go up to $1,750,000 under the following circumstances: (1) The small business has been approved for an IT loan, and (2) the business has applied for a separate working capital loan (or loans) under EWCP and/or other 7(a) loan programs. When there is an IT loan and a separate working capital loan, the maximum SBA guaranty on the combined loans can be up to $1,750,000 as long as the SBA guaranty on the working capital loan does not exceed $1,250,000. In all cases, to receive the maximum SBA guaranty amount of $1,750,000, the financing package for the small business must include an IT loan that was approved after December 7, 2004.

For the International trade Loan, SBA can guaranty up to 85 percent of loans of $150,000 and less, and up to 75 percent of loans above $150,000. The maximum guaranteed amount is $1,250,000.

Only collateral located in the United States, its territories and possessions is acceptable as collateral under this program. The lender must take a first lien position (or first mortgage) on items financed under an international

trade loan. Additional collateral may be required, including personal guarantees, subordinate liens, or items that are not financed by the loan proceeds.
www.sba.gov/financing/loanprog/tradeloans.html

Defense Loan and Technical Assistance (DELTA) Program
SBA's Defense Economic Transition Assistance program is designed to help eligible small business contractors to transition from defense to civilian markets.
A small business is eligible if it has been detrimentally impacted by the closure (or substantial reduction) of a Department of Defense (DoD) installation, or the termination (or substantial reduction) of a Department of Defense Program on which the small business was a prime contractor, subcontractor, or supplier at any tier. In addition a business can be deemed eligible if it is located in community that has been detrimentally impacted by these same actions.
The DELTA program provides financial and technical assistance to defense-dependent small businesses, which have been adversely affected by defense reductions. The goal of the program is to assist these businesses to diversify into the commercial market while remaining part of the defense industrial base. Complete information on eligibility and other rules is available from each SBA district office.
This program can be used in conjunction with both SBA's 7(a) and 504 Loan Programs and generally follows the provisions of each program. In order to be eligible for this program, small businesses must derive at least 25 percent of its revenues from Department of Defense or defense-related Department of Energy contracts or subcontracts in support of defense prime contracts in any one of five prior operating years.
Small businesses interested in utilizing this program must also meet at least one of the program's policy objectives:

- Job creation --- creates job opportunities and new economic activities in impacted communities
- Plant retooling and expansion ---modernizes or expands the plant and enables it to remain available to the Department of Defense.

www.sba.gov/financing/loanp

US Community Adjustment and Investment Program (CAIP)
CAIP is a program established to assist U.S. c
ompanies that are doing business in areas of the country that have been negatively affected by NAFTA. Funds administered by Treasury (see below) allow for the payment of fees on eligible loans. These fees include the 7(a) program guarantee fee (and subsidy) and the 504 program guarantee, CDC and lender fees. Depending on the loan size, the fees can be sizeable.
The CAIP works with the SBA in both their 7(a) Loan Guarantee Program and 504 Program to reduce borrower costs and increase the availability of these proven business assistance programs. CAIP can be used with both the 7(a) and 504 Loan Programs
To be eligible, certain criteria must be met; for example, the business must reside in a county noted as being negatively affected by NAFTA, based on job losses and the unemployment rate of the county; this was recently expanded to allow for granting eligibility to defined areas within a county (which will allow SBA to react quickly in offering to provide assistance when, for example, a plant closes).
In addition, there is a job creation component. For 7(a) loans, one job has to be created for every $70,000 SBA guarantees. For 504 loans, one job has to be created for every $50,000 SBA guarantees. Currently, over 230 counties in 29 states are designated as eligible.
www.sba.gov/financing/loanprog/caip.html

Qualified Employee Trusts Loan Program
The objective of this program is to provide financial assistance to Employee Stock Ownership Plans. The employee trust must be part of a plan sponsored by the employer company and qualified under regulations set by either the Internal Revenue Service Code (as an Employee Stock Ownership Plan or ESOP) or the Department of Labor (the Employee Retirement Income Security Act or ERISA). Applicants covered by the ERISA regulations must also secure an exemption from the Department of Labor regulations prohibiting certain loan transactions.
Effective December 22, 2000, a maximum loan amount of $2 million has been established for 7(a) loans. However, the maximum dollar amount the SBA can guaranty is generally $1 million. Small loans carry a maximum guaranty

of 85 percent. Loans are considered small if the gross loan amount is $150,000 or less. For loans greater than $150,000, the maximum guaranty is 75 percent.

SBA can assist qualified employee trusts that meet the requirements and conditions for an Employee Stock Ownership Plan (ESOP) as prescribed in all applicable IRS, Treasury, and Department of Labor regulations. The small business must provide all the funds needed to collaterize and repay the loan. A qualified employee trust may:

- re-lend proceeds to the employer by purchasing qualified employer securities, or
- purchase a controlling interest in the employer.

www.sba.gov/financing/loanprog/trusts.html

Pollution Control Loan Program
Pollution Control Loans are 7(a) loans with a special purpose of pollution control. The program is designed to provide financing to eligible small businesses for the planning, design, or installation of a pollution control facility. This facility must prevent, reduce, abate, or control any form of pollution, including recycling. This program follows the 7(a) guidelines with the following exception. Use of proceeds must be for fixed-assets only.
www.sba.gov/financing/loanprog/pollution.html

CAPLines Loan Program
CAPLines is the umbrella program under which the SBA helps small businesses meet their short-term and cyclical working capital needs. A CAPLines loan, Except the Small Asset-Based Line, can be for any dollar amount that does not exceed SBA's limit. (See the 7(a) Loan program for more information on SBA's Basic Requirements.) There are five short-term working-capital loan programs for small businesses under the CAPLines umbrella:

SEASONAL LINE: These are advances against anticipated inventory and accounts receivable help during peak seasons when businesses experience seasonal sales fluctuations. Can be revolving or non-revolving.

CONTRACT LINE: Finances the direct labor and material cost associated with performing assignable contract(s). Can be revolving or non-revolving.

BUILDERS LINE: If you are a small general contractor or builder constructing or renovating commercial or residential buildings, this can finance direct labor-and material costs. The building project serves as the collateral, and loans can be revolving or non-revolving.

STANDARD ASSET-BASED LINE: This is an asset-based revolving line of credit for businesses unable to meet credit standards associated with long-term credit. It provides financing for cyclical growth, recurring and/or short-term needs. Repayment comes from converting short-term assets into cash, which is remitted to the lender. Businesses continually draw from this line of credit, based on existing assets, and repay as their cash cycle dictates. This line generally is used by businesses that provide credit to other businesses. Because these loans require continual servicing and monitoring of collateral, the lender may charge additional fees.

SMALL ASSET-BASED LINE: This is an asset-based revolving line of credit of up to $200,000. It operates like a standard asset-based line except that some of the stricter servicing requirements are waived, providing the business can consistently show repayment ability from cash flow for the full amount.

Except the Small Asset-Based Line, CAPLine loans follow SBA's maximum loan amounts. The Small Asset-Based Line has a maximum loan amount of $200,000.
Although most small businesses are eligible for SBA loans, some types of businesses are ineligible and a case-by-case determination must be made by the Agency.
Each of the five lines of credit has a maturity of up to five (5) years, but, because each is tailored to an individual business's needs, a shorter initial maturity may be established. CAPLines funds can be used as needed throughout the term of the loan to purchase assets, as long as sufficient time is allowed to convert the assets into cash at maturity.
Holders of at least 20% ownership in the business are generally required to guaranty the loan. Although inadequate

collateral will not be the sole reason for denial of a loan request, the nature and value of that collateral does factor into the credit decision.
www.sba.gov/financing/loanprog/caplines.html

Certified Lenders Program (CLP)
The Certified Lenders Program (CLP) is designed to provide expeditious service on loan applications received from lenders who have a successful SBA lending track record and a thorough understanding of SBA policies and procedures. CLP lenders are expected to perform a complete analysis of the application and, in return, SBA promises a fast loan decision. SBA reviews the lender's credit analysis rather than conducts a second analysis. SBA still makes the final credit and eligibility decision but, by completing a credit review instead of an independently conducting analysis, SBA strives for 3-day (working days) turn around in arriving at its decision.
The key aspect of CLP is the greater utilization of the credit knowledge of the lender's loan officers to shorten SBA's loan processing time. SBA still makes an independent determination as to whether the applicant can repay the loan from the profits of the business, but under CLP, the lenders work is reviewed rather than completely double-checked.
To become a Certified Lender, an SBA field office may nominate a Lender. A Lender may also request a field office to consider it for CLP status. SBA district directors may approve and renew a Lender's CLP status.
If the district director does not approve a request for CLP status, the Lender may appeal to the Associate Administrator of Financial Assistance, whose decision will be final. If SBA grants CLP status, it applies only in the field office that processed the CLP designation. A CLP Lender must execute a Supplemental Guarantee Agreement that will specify a term not to exceed two years.
www.sba.gov/financing/lendinvest/clp.html

Preferred Lenders Program (PLP)
The Preferred Lenders Program (PLP) is another step in SBA's process of "streamlining" the procedures necessary to provide financial assistance to the small business community. Under PLP, SBA delegates loan approval, closing, and most servicing and liquidation authority and responsibility to these carefully selected lenders. . (Lenders new to SBA should first read about becoming an SBA Lender) SBA will continue to check loan eligibility criteria under this program.
PLP lenders are nominated based on their historical record with the Agency. They must have demonstrated a proficiency in processing and servicing SBA-guaranteed loans. The credit criteria for PLP loans are the same as that for the CLP and/or the Regular 7(a) program. In the event of payment default by the borrower and the need for enforced collections, the PLP lender agrees to liquidate all business assets before asking SBA to honor its guaranty.
To become a Preferred Lender, an SBA field office may nominate a Lender. A Lender may also request a field office to consider it for PLP status. The SBA field office will forward its recommendation to an SBA centralized loan processing center which will submit its recommendation and supporting documentation to the Associate Administrator of Financial Assistance (AA/FA) for final decision.
If the Lender is approved, the AA/FA will designate the area in which it can make PLP loans. Before it can operate as a PLP Lender, the approved Lender must execute a Supplemental Guarantee Agreement, which will specify a term not to exceed two years. When a PLP's Supplemental Guarantee Agreement expires, SBA may recertify it as a PLP Lender for an additional term not to exceed two years. Prior to recertification, SBA will review a PLP Lender's loans, policies and procedures. The recertification decision of the AA/FA is final.
A PLP Lender may request an expansion of the territory in which it can process PLP loans by submitting its request to a loan-processing center. The center will obtain the recommendation of each SBA office in the area into which the PLP Lender would like to expand its PLP operations. The center will forward the recommendations to the AA/FA for final decision. If a PLP Lender is not a CLP Lender in a territory into which it seeks to expand its PLP status, it automatically obtains CLP status in that territory when it is granted PLP status for the territory.
Because of the expanded authority and the expedited nature of the PLP program, certain loans cannot be processed under the PLP Program. A PLP Lender should consult SBA's SOP, and or the PLP Loan Processing Center for these guidelines.
www.sba.gov/financing/lendinvest/plp.html

SBAExpress

Maximum Loan Amount:	$350,000
Maximum SBAGuaranty %:	50%
Interest Rate:	Lenders and borrowers can negotiate the interest rate. Rates are tied to the prime rate (as published in the Wall Street Journal) and may be fixed or variable, but they may not exceed SBA maximums: Lenders may charge up to 6.5 percent over prime rate for loans of $50,000 or less and up to 4.5 percent over the prime rate for loans over $50,000
Eligibility Decision:	By SBA, Qualified Lenders May be granted Authorization to make eligibility determinations
Revolving Lines of Credit:	SBAExpress allows revolving loans up to 7 years with maturity extensions permitted at the outset
Turnaround Time:	Within 36 Hours
Forms:	Lender Uses Mostly Own Forms and Procedures
Collateral:	Lenders are not required to take collateral for loans up to $25,000. Lenders may use their existing collateral policy for loans over $25,000 up to $150,000. For Loans greater than $150,000, follows SBA's general collateral policy
Credit Decision:	By Lender
Purchase:	May request expedited SBA purchase on small loans or in situations where liquidation may be delayed.

Lender Participation

A lender may be eligible to participate in SBAExpress if one of the following:

- Currently participate with SBA and meet certain portfolio performance standards. There are no minimum SBA loan volume requirements to begin making SBAExpress loans.
- Are a non-SBA lender that currently makes a reasonable number commercial loans of $50,000 or less, and
- Loans made under this program generally follow SBA's standards for Size, Use of Proceeds, Type of Business and Availability of Funds. Differences unique to SBAExpress are noted below. Contact your SBA district office for more information.

Lenders may use SBAExpress only for 7(a) loans and not for the microloan program, the development company program (504), or for LowDoc loans or any other SBA pilot program loans, unless specifically allowed by that pilot. In addition the following loans or loan programs are not allowed under SBAExpress:

- Disabled Assistance Loan Program (DAL)
- Energy Conservation
- International Trade, except for Export Express loans described in further detail in section 11 below
- Qualified Employee Trusts (ESOP)
- Pollution Control Program
- Defense Loan and Technical Assistance (DELTA)
- CapLines Program (including Builders Loan Program)
- Community Investment Adjustment Program (CAIP)

SBAExpress loans cannot be made to:

- Agricultural and farm businesses
- Fishing and shore operations (including commercial fishing activities and the construction of new fishing vessels)
- Medical facilities involving any type of extended care/assisted living situation. (These could be eligible for standard 7(a) loan processing, but additional analysis would be required, which would preclude SBAExpress' expedited handling.) Routine medical laboratories/facilities, physician/dental offices, veterinarians, etc., are eligible for SBAExpress processing
- Mines (including sand and gravel pits)
- Applicants with operations, facilities, or offices located overseas (other than those strictly associated with the marketing and/or distribution of products exported from the U.S.)

- Businesses engaged in teaching, instructing, counseling or indoctrinating religion or religious beliefs, whether in a religious or secular setting (Businesses engaged in moderate such activity could be eligible for standard 7(a) loan processing, but additional analysis would be required, which would preclude SBAExpress' expedited procedures.)
- A business deriving directly or indirectly more than de minims gross revenue through the sale of products or services, or the presentation of any depiction or displays, of a prurient sexual nature or that presents any live performances of a prurient nature.

www.sba.gov/financing/lendinvest/sbaexpress.html

CommunityExpress

CommunityExpress is a pilot SBA loan program that was developed in collaboration with the National Community Reinvestment Coalition (NCRC) and its member organizations. Under the pilot, which is available to selected lenders, an SBAExpress like program will be offered to pre-designated geographic areas serving mostly Low and Moderate Income areas and New Markets small businesses. The program will also include technical and management assistance, which is designed to help increase the loan applicant's chances of success.

Maximum Loan Amount:	$250,000
Maximum SBAGuaranty %:	Follows Standard SBA Guaranty Percent
Interest Rate:	CommunityExpress loans are subject to the same maximum interest rate as all SBA loans
Eligibility Decision:	By SBA
Revolving Lines of Credit:	Allows revolving loans up to 7 years
Turnaround Time:	Mostly Within 36 Hours
Forms:	Lender Uses Mostly Own Forms and Procedures
Collateral:	Lenders are not required to take collateral for loans up to $25,000. Lenders may use their existing collateral policy for loans over $25,000 up to $150,000. For Loans greater than $150,000, follows SBA's general collateral policy
Credit Decision:	By Lender
Technical Assistance:	Arranged or Provided by Lender

The SBA initiated the CommunityExpress program in May of 1999 with about 10 NCRC lenders. The Agency is now expanding the program to PLP lenders that have at least a 90 percent currency rate on their SBA 7(a) portfolio for the last 3 fiscal years and to selected non-PLP lenders that meet the eligibility requirements for participating in the SBAExpress program.

Both the NCRC and the SBA as often crucial to the success of these businesses have recognized technical Assistance. As a result, the CommunityExpress program includes a specific technical assistance component. Borrowers must receive pre- and post-loan closing technical and management assistance from local non-profit providers and/or from participating lenders, with that assistance coordinated, arranged and, when necessary, paid for by CommunityExpress lenders. CommunityExpress lenders may also consider this technical assistance as a collateral enhancement.

CommunityExpress lenders must establish (and document) an internal procedure to ensure the consistent delivery of appropriate and effective technical and management assistance. The process begins with the identification of qualified and committed T/A providers. The focus then shifts to the CommunityExpress applicant and the T/A provider's development of a business plan (as appropriate) and an assessment of the applicant's management and technical assistance strengths and weaknesses. If weaknesses are identified as a result of that assessment, the lender should document the T/A provider's recommendations and the remedial plan. The lender, in cooperation with the T/A provider, is also expected to strongly encourage the applicant to follow that plan.

CommunityExpress loans must meet the basic 7(a) loan criteria except where differences specified below:

Types of Loans Not Allowable for CommunityExpress

- Disabled Assistance Loan Program (DAL)
- Energy Conservation
- International Trade

- Qualified Employee Trusts (ESOP)
- Pollution Control Program
- Defense Loan and Technical Assistance (DELTA)
- Export Working Capital Program (EWCP); and
- CapLines Program (including Builders Loan Program)

Types of Businesses Not Allowable for CommunityExpress

- Agricultural and farm businesses
- Fishing and shore operations (including commercial fishing activities and the construction of new fishing vessels)
- Medical facilities (including residential care facilities)
- Mines (including sand and gravel pits)
- Applicants doing business in foreign countries
- Businesses engaged in teaching, instructing, counseling or indoctrinating religion or religious beliefs, whether in a religious or secular setting; and,
- A business with any products or services of a sexual nature.

www.sba.gov/financing/lendinvest/comexpress.html

SBA'S Secondary Market Program

There is an active secondary market in the loans guaranteed by the Small Business Administration. This market was created to increase the attractiveness of small business lending to the lending community. Through the market, lenders are able to sell the guaranteed portion of SBA guaranteed loans to investors and thereby improve their liquidity and increase their yield on the un-guaranteed portion of SBA loans.

In addition, the secondary market provides a hedge against future liquidity problems because the guaranteed portion of an SBA guaranteed the lender might readily sell portfolio. The market also allows a lender to meet the credit needs of a local small business community by importing capital from other parts of the country. Additional information on SBA's secondary market program is available from SBA's Secondary Market and 504 Sales Branch on (202) 205-6024.

www.sba.gov/financing/lendinvest/marketprog.html

Asset Sales

The SBA's Asset Sales program is an initiative to sell the agency's "owned portfolio" of loans and other assets. These assets consist of Section 7(a) and 504 guaranteed loans purchased, Section 7(a) and disaster assistance direct loans, and other liquidation assets, such as collateral acquired as a result of liquidation.

The Asset Sales Program is a prudent portfolio tool to assist in managing the SBA's overall credit exposure. It allows the SBA to take advantage of the efficiencies of the private sector, reduce the intense resource demands of loan and owned asset servicing, and allow existing resources to be deployed in mission-critical areas necessary to achieving the SBA's vision.

www.sba.gov/financing/lendinvest/asset.html

SMALL BUSINESS ADMINISTRATION REGION, BRANCH and DISTRICT OFFICES

The Small Business Administration region offices are branch operations of the SBA who work to provide aid, counseling and protect the interests of small business concerns. (Note: All addresses and phone numbers are subject to change)

CENTRAL
HEADQUARTERS
409 Third Street SW
Washington, DC 20416
(202) 205-6410

REGION I
Connecticut
Maine
Massachusetts
New Hampshire
Rhode Island
Vermont

Region I Office
10 Causeway St, Ste 812
Boston, MA 02222-1093
(617) 565-8416
Fax (617) 565-8420

Region I
Branch and District Offices
Connecticut District Office
330 Main St, 2nd Fl
Hartford, CT 06106
(860) 240-4700

New Hampshire District Office
JC Cleveland Fed Bldg
55 Pleasant St, Ste 3101
Concord, NH 03301
(603) 225-1400
Fax (603) 225-1409

Boston District Office
10 Causeway St, Rm 265
Boston, MA 02222
(617) 565-5590

Springfield Branch Office
STCC Technology Park
One Federal Street Building 101-R
Springfield, MA 01105
(413) 785-0484

Maine District Office
Edmund S Muskie Federal Bldg, Rm 512
68 Sewall St
Augusta, ME 04330
(207) 622-8551

Rhode Island District Office
380 Westminster St, Rm 511
Providence, RI 02903
(401) 528-4561

Vermont District Office
87 State St, Rm 205
Montpelier, VT 05601
(802) 828-4422

REGION II
New Jersey
New York
Puerto Rico
Virgin Islands

Region II Office
26 Federal Plaza, Ste 3108
New York, NY 10278
(212) 264-1450

Region II
Branch and District Offices
New Jersey District Office
Two Gateway Center, 15th Fl
Newark, NJ 07102
(973) 645-2434

Buffalo District Office
Niagara Center
130 S Elmwood Ave, Ste 540
Buffalo, NY 14202
(716) 551-4301
Fax (716) 551-4418

Rochester Branch Office
100 State Street, Rm 410
Rochester, NY 14614
(585) 263-6700
Fax (585) 263-3146

New York District Office
26 Federal Plaza, Ste 3100
New York, NY 10278
(212) 264-4354
Fax (212) 264-4963

Long Island Branch Office
350 Motor Parkway, Ste 109
Hauppauge, NY 11788
(631) 454-0750
Fax (631) 454-0769

Syracuse District Office
401 S Salina St, 5th Fl
Syracuse, NY 13202
(315) 471-9393
Fax (315) 471-9288

Elmira Branch Office
333 E. Water Street, 4th floor
Elmira, NY 14901
(607) 734-8130
Fax (607) 733-4656

Puerto Rico District Office
252 Ponce de Leon Ave
Citibank Tower, Ste 200
San Juan, PR 00918
(787) 766-5572 or (800) 669-8049
Fax (787) 766-5309

St Croix Post of Duty
Almeric L. Christian Federal Building & U.S. Court House
3013 Estate Golden Rock rm 167
Christiansted, St. Croix, USVI 00820
(340) 778-5380 or (800)669-8049
Fax (340)778-1102

REGION III
Delaware
Washington, DC
Maryland
Pennsylvania
Virginia
West Virginia

Region III Office
Parkview Tower
1150 First Avenue- Ste 1001
King of Prussia, PA 19406
(610) 382-3092

Region III
Branch and District Offices
Washington, DC District Office
740 15th St NW, suite 300
Washington, DC 20005-3544
(202) 272-0345

Deleware District Office
1007 N Orange St, Ste 1120
Wilmington, DE 19801-1232
(302) 573-6294

Maryland District Office
City Crescent Bldg, 6th Fl
10 South Howard St
Baltimore, MD 21201
(410) 962-6195

Philadelphia District Office
Parkview Tower
1150 First Avenue- Ste 1001
King of Prussia, PA 19406
(610) 382-3062

Pittsburgh District Office
411 Seventh Ave, Ste 1450
Pittsburgh, PA 15219
(412) 395-6560

Virginia District Office
400 North 8th St
Federal Bldg, Ste 1150
Richmond, VA 23219-4829
(804) 771-2400
Fax (804) 771-2764

West Virginia District Office
320 West Pike St, Ste 330
Clarksburg, WV 26301
(304) 623-5631

Charleston Branch Office
405 Capital Street Ste 412
Charleston, WV 25301
(304) 347-5220

REGION IV
Alabama
Florida
Georgia
Kentucky
Mississippi
North Carolina
South Carolina
Tennessee

Region IV Office
233 Peachtree St NE, Ste 1800
Atlanta, GA 30303
(404) 331-4999
Fax (404) 331-2354

Region IV
District and Branch Offices
Alabama District Office
801 Tom Martin Drive, Ste 201
Birmingham, AL 35211
(205) 290-7101
Fax (205) 290-7404

Jacksonville District Office
7825 Baymeadows Way, Ste 100B
Jacksonville, FL 32256-7504
(904) 443-1900

Miami District Office
100 S Biscayne Blvd, 7th Fl
Miami, FL 33131
(305) 536-5521
Fax (305) 536-5058

Georgia District Office
233 Peachtree St NE, Ste 1900
Atlanta, GA 30303
(404) 331-0100

Kentucky District Office
600 Dr MLK Jr PL, Rm 188
Louisville, KY 40202-2254
(502) 582-5971

Jackson District Office
Regions Plaza
210 E Capitol St, Ste 900
Jackson, MS 39201
(601) 965-4378
Fax (601) 965-5629

Gulfport Branch Office
Hancock Bank Plaza
2510 14th Street, Ste103
Gulfport, MS 39501
(228) 863-4449
Fax (228) 864-0179

North Carolina District Office
6302 Fairview Rd, Ste 300
Charlotte, NC 28210-2227
(704) 344-6563
Fax (704) 344-6769

South Carolina District Office
1835 Assembly St, Rm 1425
Columbia, SC 29201
(803) 765-5377
Fax (803) 765-5962

Tennessee District Office
50 Vantage Way, Ste 201
Nashville, TN 37228
(615) 736-5881
Fax (615) 736-7232
TTY/TDD (615) 736-2499

REGION V
Illinois
Indiana
Michigan
Minnesota
Ohio
Wisconsin

Region V Office
500 West Madison St
Citicorp Center, Ste 1240
Chicago, IL 60661-2511
(312) 353-0357
Fax (312) 353-3426

Region V
District and Branch Offices
Illinois District Office
500 W Madison St, Ste 1250
Chicago, IL 60661-2511
(312) 353-4528
Fax (312) 866-5688

Illinois District Office
3330 Ginger Crk Rd, Ste B
Springfield, IL 62711
(217) 793-5020
Fax (217) 793-5025

Indiana District Office
8500 Keystone Crossing, Suite 400
Indianapolis, IN 46240-2460
(317) 226-7272

Cleveland, OH District Office
1350 Euclid Ave, Ste 211
Cleveland, OH 44115
(216) 522-4180
Fax (216) 522-2038

Columbus, OH District Office
401 N Front St, Ste 200
Columbus, Ohio 43215
(614) 469-6860

Michigan District Office
477 Michigan Ave
Ste 515, McNamara Bldg
Detroit, MI 48226
(313) 226-6075

Minnesota District Office
100 North Sixth St
Ste 210-C Butler Sq
Minneapolis, MN 55403
(612)370-2324

Wisconsin District Office
740 Regent St, Ste 100
Madison, WI 53715
(608) 441-5263
Fax (608) 441-5541

Wisconsin District Office
310 West Wisconsin Ave, Rm 400
Milwaukee, WI 53203
(414) 297-3941
Fax (414) 297-1377

REGION VI
Arkansas
Louisiana
New Mexico
Oklahoma
Texas

Region VI Office
4300 Amon Carter Blvd, Ste 108
Fort Worth, TX 76155
(817) 684-5581
Fax (817) 684-5588

Region VI
District and Branch Offices
Arkansas District Office
2120 Riverfront Drive, Ste 250
Little Rock, AR 72202-1796
(501) 324-7379
Fax (501) 324-7394

Louisiana District Office
365 Canal St, Ste 2820
New Orleans, LA 70130
(504) 589-6685

New Mexico District Office
625 Silver SW, Ste 320
Albuquerque, NM 87102
(505) 248-8225
Fax (505) 248-8246

Oklahoma District Office
Federal Bldg
301 NW 6th St
Oklahoma City, OK 73102
(405) 609-8000

Dallas/Fort Worth District Office
4300 Amon Carter Blvd, Ste 114
Fort Worth, TX 76155
(817) 684-5500
Fax (817) 684-5516

El Paso District Office
211 N. Florence Street Ste 201
El Paso, TX 79901
(915) 834-4600
Fax (915) 834-4689

Harlingen District Office
222 East Van Buren Ave, Ste 500
Harlingen, TX 78550
(956) 427-8533
Fax (956) 427-8537

Houston District Office
8701 S Gessner Dr, Ste 1200
Houston, TX 77074
(713) 773-6500
Fax (713) 773-6550

Lubbock District Office
1205 Texas Ave, Rm 408
Lubbock, TX 79401-2693
(806) 472-7462
Fax (806) 472-7487

San Antonio District Office
17319 San Pedro, Ste 200
San Antonio, TX 78232-1411
(210) 403-5900
Fax (210) 403-5936
TDD (210) 403-5933

REGION VII
Iowa
Kansas
Missouri
Nebraska

Region VII Office
1000 Walnut suite 530
Kansas City, MO 64106
(816) 426-4840
Fax (816) 426-4848

Region VII
District and Branch Offices
Des Moines District Office
210 Walnut St, Rm 749
Des Moines, IA 50309-4106
(515) 284-4422

Cedar Rapids Branch Office
2750 1st Ave NE, Ste 350
Cedar Rapids, IA 52402-4831
(319) 362-6405

Kansas District Office
271 W 3rd St N, Ste 2500
Wichita, KS 67202
(316) 269-6616

St Louis District Office
200 North Broadway, Ste 1500
St Louis, MO 63102
(314) 539-6600
Fax (314) 539-3785

Kansas City District Office
1000 Walnut, Ste 500
Kansas City, MO 64106
(816) 426-4900

Nebraska District Office
10675 Bedford Ave, Ste 100
Omaha, NE 68134
(402) 221-4691

REGION VIII
Colorado
Montana
North Dakota
South Dakota
Utah
Wyoming

Region VIII Office
721 19th St, Ste 400
Denver, CO 80202-2599
(303) 844-0500
Fax (303) 844-0506
TTY/TDD (303) 844-0507

Region VIII
District and Branch Offices
Colorado District Office
721 19th St, Ste 426
Denver, CO 80202
(303) 844-2607

Montana District Office
10 West 15th St, Ste 1100
Helena, MT 59626
(406) 441-1081
Fax (406) 441-1090

North Dakota District Office
657 Second Ave N, Rm 218
PO Box 3086
Fargo, ND 58108-3086
(701) 239-5131
Fax (701) 239-5645

South Dakota District Office
2329 N Career Ave, Ste 105
Sioux Falls, SD 57107
(605) 330-4243
Fax (605) 330-4215
TTY/TDD (605) 331-3527

Utah District Office
125 South State St, Rm 2227
Salt Lake City, UT 84138
(801) 524-3209

Wyoming District Office
100 East B St, Fed Bldg, Rm 4001
PO Box 44001
Casper, WY 82602-5013
(800) 776-9144 ext 1

REGION IX
Arizona
California
Guam
Hawaii
Nevada

Region IX Office
330 North Brand Blvd, Ste 1270
Glendale, CA 91203-2304
(818) 552-3434
Fax (818) 552-3440

Region IX
District and Branch Offices
Arizona District Office
2828 North Central Ave, Ste 800
Phoenix, AZ 85004-1093
(602) 745-7200
Fax (602) 745-7210

Fresno District Office
2719 North Air Fresno Dr, Ste 200
Fresno, CA 93727
(559) 487-5791
Fax (559) 487-5636

Los Angeles District Office
330 North Brand, Ste 1200
Glendale, CA 91203
(818) 552-3215

Sacramento District Office
6501 Sylvan Road Ste 100
Citrus Height, CA 95610
(916) 735-1700
Fax (916) 735-1719

San Diego District Office
550 West C St, Ste 550
San Diego, CA 92101
(619) 557-7250
Fax (619) 557-5894

San Francisco District Office
455 Market St, 6th Fl
San Francisco, CA 94105-2420
(415) 744-6820

Santa Ana District Office
200 W Santa Ana Blvd, Ste 700
Santa Ana, CA 92701
(714) 550-7420
Fax (714) 550-0191

Hawaii District Office
300 Ala Moana Blvd ,Rm 2-235
Box 50207
Honolulu, HI 96850
(808) 541-2990
Fax (808) 541-2976

Nevada District Office
400 South 4th St, Ste 250
Las Vegas, NV 89101
(702) 388-6611
Fax (702) 388-6469

Guam District Office
400 Route 8, Ste 302
First Hawaiian Bank Bldg
Mongmong, GU 96927
(671) 472-7419
Fax (671) 472-7365

REGION X
Alaska
Idaho
Oregon
Washington

Region X Office
2401 Fourth Ave, Ste 400
Seattle, WA 98121
(206) 553-5676
Fax (206) 553-4155

Region X
District and Branch Offices
Alaska District Office
510 L St, Ste 310
Anchorage, AK 99501-1952
(907) 271-4022

Boise District Office
380 East Parkcenter Blvd, Ste 330
Boise, ID 83706
(208) 334-1696
Fax (208) 334-9353

Oregon District Office
601 SW 2nd Ave, Ste 950
Portland, OR 97204-3192
(503) 326-2682
Fax (503) 326-2808

Seattle, WA District Office
2401 Fourth Ave, Ste 450
Seattle, WA 98121
(206) 553-7310

Spokane, WA Branch Office
801 W Riverside Ave, Ste 200
Spokane, WA 99201
(509) 353-2800

SELECTED SMALL BUSINESS DEVELOPMENT CENTERS (SBDC)

Small Business Development Centers provide management assistance to current and prospective small business owners.
Note: All addresses and phone numbers are subject to change

ALABAMA
University of Alabama-Birmingham
1500 1st Avenue N R118
Birmingham, AL 35203
(205)307-6510
Fax (205) 307-6511
www.asbdc.org

ALASKA
University of Alaska - Anchorage
430 W Seventh Ave, Ste 110
Anchorage, AK 99501-3550
(907) 274-7232
Fax (907) 274-9524
www.aksbdc.org

AMERICAN SAMOA
American Samoa Comm College
PO Box 2609
Pago Pago, Am Samoa 96799
011 (684) 699-4830
Fax 011 (684) 699-6132
www.as-sbdc.org

ARIZONA
Maricopa County Comm College
2411 W 14th St, Ste114
Tempe, AZ 85281
(480) 731-8722
Fax (480) 731-8729
www.azsbdc.net/Default.aspx

ARKANSAS
University of Arkansas-Little Rock
2801 S University Ave rm 260
Little Rock, AR 72204
(501) 683-7700
Fax (501) 683-7720
http://asbdc.ualr.edu

CALIFORNIA
For a complete list of California SBDCs, please visit the State of California Commerce & Economic Development
www.calbusiness.ca.gov/cedpgybsbdc.asp

Santa Ana SBDC
Tri-County Lead SBDC
Callifornia State Univ - Fullerton
800 N State College Blvd, LH640
Fullerton, CA 92834
(714) 278-2719
Fax (714) 278-7858
www.leadsbdc.org

San Diego SBDC
SW Community College District
900 Otay Lakes Rd bldg 1681
Chula Vista, CA 91910
(619) 482-6388
Fax (619) 482-6402
www.sbditc.org

Fresno SBDC
UC Merced Lead Center
University of California - Merced
550 E Shaw, Ste 100
Fresno, CA 93710-7702
(559) 241-6590
Fax (559) 241-7422
http://sbdc.ucmerced.edu

Sacramento SBDC
Callifornia State Univer - Chico
35 Main Street room 203
Chico, CA 95929-0765
(530) 898-4598
Fax (530) 898-4734
www.necsbdc.org

San Francisco SBDC
N California SBDC Lead Center
Humboldt State University
Office of Economic Development
1 Harpst St
Arcata, CA, 95521
(707) 826-3920
http://www.norcalsbdc.org

Los Angeles Region SBDC
Long Beach Comm College Dist
3950 Paramount Blvd, Ste 101
Lakewood, CA 90712
(562) 938-5004
Fax (562) 938-5030
www.lasbdcnet.ibcc.edu/lead.html

COLORADO
Office of Economic Development
1625 Broadway, Ste 2700
Denver, CO 80202
(303) 892-3864
Fax (303) 892-3848
www.coloradosbdc.org

CONNECTICUT
University of Central Connecticut
185 Main Street
New Britain, CT 06051
(860) 827-7104
Fax (860) 827-7112
www.ccsu.edu/sbdc/

DELAWARE
Delaware Technology Park
1 Innovation Way, Ste 301
Newark, DE 19711
(302) 831-1555
Fax (302) 831-1423
www.delawaresbdc.org

DISTRICT OF COLUMBIA
Howard University School of Business
2600 6th St NW, Rm 128
Washington, DC 20059
(202) 806-1550
Fax (202) 806-1777
www.dcsbdc.com

FLORIDA
University of West Florida
401 E Chase St, Ste 100
Pensacola, FL 32502-6160
(850) 473-7800
Fax (850) 473-7813
www.floridasbdc.com

GEORGIA
University of Georgia
1180 E Broad St
Athens, GA 30602-5412
(706) 542-2762
Fax (706) 542-7935
www.georgiasbdc.org

HAWAII
University of Hawaii at Hilo
308 Kamehameha Ave, Ste 201
Hilo, HI 96720-2960
(808) 974-7515
Fax (808) 974-7683
www.hawaii-sbdc.org

IDAHO
Boise State University
1910 University Dr
Boise, ID 83725-1655
(208) 426-3799
Fax (208) 426-3877
www.idahosbdc.org

ILLINOIS
Department of Commerce &
Economic Opportunity
620 E Adams St 4th floor
Springfield, IL 62701-1615
(217) 524-5700
Fax (217) 524-0171
www.ilsbdc.biz

INDIANA
Indiana Economic Dev Corp
One N Capitol, Ste 900
Indianapolis, IN 46204-2043
(317) 234-2086
Fax (317) 232-8872
www.isbdc.org

IOWA
Iowa State University
340 Gerdin Business Bldg
Ames, IA 50011-1350
(515) 294-2030
Fax (515) 294-6522
www.iowasbdc.org.

KANSAS
Fort Hays State University
214 SW Sixth St, Ste 301
Topeka, KS 66603-3719
(785) 296-6514
Fax (785) 291-3261
www.fhsu.edu/ksbdc

KENTUCKY
University of Kentucky
225 Gatton Bus & Economic Bldg
Lexington, KY 40506-0034
(859) 257-7668
Fax (859) 323-1907
www.ksbdc.org

LOUISIANA
University of Louisiana - Monroe
College of Business Admin
700 University Ave
Monroe, LA 71209-6435
(318) 342-5506
Fax (318) 342-5510
www.lsbdc.org

MAINE
University of Southern Maine
96 Falmouth St
PO Box 9300
Portland, ME 04103-930
(207) 780-4420
Fax (207) 780-4810
www.mainesbdc.org

MARYLAND
University of Maryland
7100 Baltimore Ave, Ste 401
College Park, MD 20740-3640
(301) 403-8300 ext.15
Fax (301) 403-8303
www.mdsbdc.umd.edu

MASSACHUSETTS
University of Massachusetts
227 Isenberg School of
Management
121 President's Drive
Amherst, MA 01003-4935
(413) 545-6301
Fax (413) 545-1273
www.msbdc.org

MICHIGAN
Grand Valley State University
510 W Fulton Ave
Grand Rapids, MI 49504
(616) 331-7480
Fax (616) 331-7358
www.misbtdc.org

MINNESOTA
Minnesota Small Bus Dev Center
1st National Bank Bldg
332 Minnesota St, Ste E200
St Paul, MN 55101-1351
(651) 297-5770
Fax (651) 296-5287
www.mnsbdc.com

MISSISSIPPI
University of Mississippi
B-19 Jeanette Phillips Dr
PO Box 1848
University, MS 38677-1848
(662) 915-5001
Fax (662) 915-5650
www.mssbdc.org

MISSOURI
Univeristy of Missouri
410 S Sixth Street
200 Engineering North
Columbia, MO 65211
(573) 882-0344
Fax (573) 884-4297
www.missouribusiness.net/sbdc/

MONTANA
Department of Commerce
301 S Park Ave, Rm 116
PO Box 200505
Helena, MT 59601
(406) 841-2746
Fax (406) 841-2728
http://sbdc.mt.gov

NEBRASKA
University of Nebraska - Omaha
415 Roskens Hall
6001 Dodge Street
Omaha, NE 68182-0248
(402) 554-2521
Fax (402) 554-3473
http://nbdc.unomaha.edu/

NEVADA
University of Nevada - Reno
Reno College of Business
Nazir AnsariBldg.032 rm 4
Reno, NV 89557-0100
(775) 784-1717
Fax (775) 784-4337
www.nsbdc.org

NEW HAMPSHIRE
University of New Hampshire
Mittmore School of Business and
Economics, UNH
110 McConnell Hall
Durham, NH 03824-3593
(603) 862-2200
Fax (603) 862-4876
www.nhsbdc.org

NEW JERSEY
Rutgers University
49 Bleeker St
Newark, NJ 07102-1993
(973) 353-1927
Fax (973) 353-1110
www.njsbdc.com

NEW MEXICO
Santa Fe Community College
6401 Richards Ave
Santa Fe, NM 87508-4887
(505) 428-1362
Fax (505) 428-1469
www.nmsbdc.org

NEW YORK
State University of New York
Corporate Woods, 3rd Floor
Albany, NY 12246-0001
(518) 443-5398
Fax (518) 443-5275
www.nyssbdc.org

NORTH CAROLINA
University of North Carolina
5 West Hargett St, Ste 600
Raleigh, NC 27601-1348
(919) 715-7272
Fax (919) 715-7777
www.sbtdc.org

NORTH DAKOTA
University of North Dakota
1600 E Century Ave, Ste 2
Bismark, ND 58501
(701) 328-5375
Fax (701) 328-5381
www.ndsbdc.org

OHIO
Ohio Department of Development
128th floor P O Box 1001
Columbus, OH 43216-1001
(614) 466-2711
Fax (614) 466-0829
www.entrepreneurohio.org

OKLAHOMA
SE Oklahoma State University
1405 N 4th Avenue, PMB 2584
Durant, OK 74701-0609
(580) 745-2877 ext 2955
Fax (580) 745-7471
www.osbdc.org

OREGON
Lane Community College
99 W Tenth Ave, Ste 390
Eugene, OR 97401-3015
(541) 463-5250
Fax (541) 345-6006
www.bizcenter.org

PACIFIC ISLANDS
University of Guam
Guam SDBC
PO Box 5014
UOG Station Mangilao
Mangilao, Guam 96923
(671) 735-2590
Fax (671) 734-2002
www.pacificsbdc.com

PENNSYLVANIA
University of Pennsylvania
The Wharton School
3733 Spruce St, Vance Hall 4th fl
Philadelphia, PA 19104-6374
(215) 898-1219
Fax (215) 573-2135
www.pasbdc.org

PUERTO RICO
Inter-American University of PR
Union Plaza Building Suite 1000
416 Ponce de Leon Ave 10th fl
Hato Rey, Puerto Rico 00918
(787) 763-6811
Fax (787) 763-6875
www.prsbdc.org

RHODE ISLAND
Johnson & Wales University
270 Weybosset St, 4th Fl
Providence, RI 02903
(401) 598-2704
Fax (401) 598-2722
www.risbdc.org

SOUTH CAROLINA
University of South Carolina
Darlamoore School of Business
1710 College St, Hipp Building
Columbia, SC 29208-9980
(803) 777-4907
Fax (803)777-4403
http://scsbdc.moore.sc.edu

SOUTH DAKOTA
University of South Dakota
Beacon School of Business
414 E Clark St, Patterson Hall
Vermillion, SD 57069
(605) 677-5287
Fax (605) 677-5427
www.sdsbdc.org

TENNESSEE
Middle Tennessee State University
615 Memorial Boulevard
Murfreesboro, Tennessee 37132
(615) 849-9999
Fax (615) 217-8548
www.tsbdc.org

TEXAS - HOUSTON
University of Houston
2302 Fannin, Ste 200
Houston, TX 77002
(713) 752-8444
Fax (713) 756-1500
http://sbdcnetwork.uh.edu

TEXAS - NORTH
Dallas County Community College
1402 Corinth St, suite 2111
Dallas, TX 75215
(214) 860-5835
Fax (214) 860-5813
www.ntsbdc.org

TEXAS - NW
Texas Tech University
2579 South Loop 289, Ste 114
Lubbock, TX 79423-1637
(806) 745-3973
Fax (806) 745-6207
www.nwtsbdc.org

TEXAS - SW TX BORDER REGION
University of Texas - San Antonio
501 West Durango Blvd
San Antonio, TX 78207-4415
(210) 458-2450
Fax (210) 458-2425
www.txsbdc.org

UTAH
Salt Lake Community College
9750 S 300 W-LHM
Salt Lake City, UT 84070
(801) 957-3481
Fax (801) 957-2007
www.utahsbdc.org

VERMONT
Vermont Technical College
P O Box 188, 1 Main Street
Randolph Center, VT 05061-0188
(802) 728-9101
Fax (802) 728-3026
www.vtsbdc.org

VIRGIN ISLANDS
University of the Virgin Islands
8000 Nisky Center, Ste 720
Charlotte Amalie
St Thomas, VI 00802-5804
(340) 776-3206
Fax (340) 775-3756
http://sbdcvi.org

VIRGINIA
George Mason University
Mason Enterprise Center
4031 University Dr, Ste 200
Fairfax, VA 22030-3409
(703) 277-7727
Fax (703) 352-8518
www.virginiasbdc.org

WASHINGTON
Washington State University
543 E Spokane Falls Blvd
PO Box 1495
Spokane, WA 99210-1495
(509) 358-7765
Fax (509) 358-7764
www.wsbdc.org

WEST VIRGINIA
West Virginia Development Office
1900 Kanawha Blvd. E.
Charleston, WV 25305
(304) 558-2960
Fax (304) 558-0127
www.sbdcwv.org

WISCONSIN
University of Wisconsin
432 North Lake St, Rm 423
Madison, WI 53706
(608) 263-7794
Fax 608-263-7830
www.wisconsinsbdc.org

WYOMING
University of Wyoming
1000 E University, Dept 3922
Laramie, WY 82979
(307) 766-3505
Fax (307) 766-3406
www.uwyo.edu/sbdc

Small Business Innovation Research Program (SBIR)

Office of Technology - Mail Code 6470
409 3rd St SW
Washington, DC 20416
(202) 205-6450
Fax (202) 205-7754

SBIR is a program that strengthens and expands the competitiveness of US small high technology research and development businesses in the federal marketplace.

SBIR Representatives of the Participating Federal Agencies

DEPARTMENT OF AGRICULTURE

www.usda.gov

Dir of Integrated Progs, Competitive Programs Unit
Cooperative State Resrch, Education Extension Svc
2434 Waterfront Centre, 800 9th St SW
Washington , DC 20024
(202) 401-1924
Fax (202) 401-1782

National Program Leader
Cooperative State Resrch, Education Extension Svc
2434 Waterfront Centre, 800 9th St SW
Washington , DC 20024
(202) 401-6852 or (202) 401-1719 or (202) 401-5823 or (202) 401-6550 or (202) 720-7536
Fax (202) 401-6070

Program Specialist
Cooperative State Resrch, Education Extension Svc
2326 Waterfront Centre, 800 9th St SW
Washington , DC 20024
(202) 401-4995
Fax (202) 401-6070

DEPARTMENT OF COMMERCE

www.noaa.gov

SBIR Program Manager, US Department of Commerce/NOAA
1335 East-West Hwy, Rm 106
Silver Spring, MD 20910
(301) 713-3565
Fax (301) 713-4100

Chief, SBIR Program Office, NIST
MS 2200
Bldg 820, Rm 306
Gaithersburg, MD 20899-0001
(301) 975-2339
Fax (301) 869-2751

Asst SBIR Program Manager/ NOAA
1335 East-West Hwy, Rm 106
Silver Spring, MD 20910
(301) 713-3565
Fax (301) 713-4100

SBIR Program Coordinator
Office of Research & Technology Applications
1335 East-West Highway, Rm 106
Silver Spring, MD 20910
(301) 713-3565
Fax (301) 713-4100

Assistant SBIR Program Manager
Technology Transfer Program/ NOAA
1335 East-West Highway, Rm 106
Silver Spring, MD 20910
(301) 713-3565
Fax (301) 713-4100

DEPARTMENT OF DEFENSE

www.dod.gov

SBIR/STTR Program Coordinator, OUSD (AT&L)
Office of Small Business Programs
201 12th Street S , suite 406
Arlington, VA 22202
(703) 604-0157 ext 146
Fax (703) 604-0025
www.acq.osd.mil/osbp/sbir

Department of the Air Force, AFRL/ XPPN
2275 D St, Bldg 16, Rm 107
Wright-Patterson, AFB, OH 45433-7217
(800) 222-0336
Fax (937) 255-2319
www.sbirsttrmall.com/portal.aspx

Joint Science and Technology for Chemical and Biological Defense (CBD)
MSC-6201 / CBT
8725 John J. Kingman Road
Ft. Belvoir, VA 22060-6201
(703)767-3307
www.armysbir.com

SBIR/STTR Program Manager
Missile Defense Agency
7100 Defense Pentagon
Washington, DC 20301-7100
(256) 955-4828
www.mda.mil

SBIR Program Coordinator
US SOCOM SOAL-T
7701 Tampa Point Blvd SOAL-KS
MacDill AFB, FL 33621-5323
(813) 828-6939
Fax (813) 828-9429

Deputy SBIR Program Manager
US Army RD &E Command
Attn: AMSRD-SS-WA-SBIR
6000 6th St, #100
Ft Belvoir, VA 22060-5608
(703) 806-2085
www.armysbir.com

Army STTR Program Manager, LTC/AC
Army Research Office
Research Triangle Park, NC 27709-2211
(919) 549-4322

Navy SBIR Program Manager
Office of Naval Research (ONR 364)
One Liberty Center
875 North Randolph Code 03TSB,Ste 1425,Rm 259
Arlington, VA 22203-1995
(703) 696-0445
Fax (703) 696-4884
www.navysbir.com

Navy STTR Program Manager
Office of Naval Research (ONR 364)
One Liberty Center
875 North Randolph Code 03TSB,Rm 261
Arlington, VA 22203-1995
(703) 696-7830
Fax (703)696-4884

SBIR Program Manager
National Geospatial-Intelligence Agency/IB
MS DN-11
12310 Sunrise Valley Dr
Reston, VA 20191
(703) 473-5183
http://nga.mil

DEPARTMENT OF EDUCATION
www.ed.gov

Institute of Education Services
National Center for Educational Research
555 New Jersey Ave SW #608D
Washington, DC 20208
(202) 208-1983
Fax (202) 219-2030

DEPARTMENT OF ENERGY
www.doe.gov

SBIR/STTR Program Manager
Office of Advanced Scientific Computing Resources
Germantown Building SC- 21.3
1000 Independence Ave SW
Washington, DC 20585-1290
(301) 903-1414
Fax (301) 903-5488

DEPT OF HEALTH & HUMAN SERVICES
www.hhs.gov

SBIR/STTR Program Coordinator
Office of Extramural Research
National Institutes of Health
6705 Rockledge Dr
RKLG I, Rm 3534
Bethesda, MD 20892
(301) 435-2688
Fax (301) 480-0146

SBIR/STTR Program Analyst
Office of Extramural Research
National Institutes of Health
6705 Rockledge Dr
RKLG I, Rm 3536
Bethesda, MD 20892
(301) 435-2713
Fax (301) 480-0146

DEPARTMENT OF HOMELAND SECURITY
www.dhs.gov

SBIR Program Manager
S&T/HSARPA HSARPA SBIR Program
Washington, DC 20528
(202) 254-6768
Fax (202) 254-7170

DEPT OF TRANSPORTATION
www.dot.gov

SBIR Program Director
Volpe Center
55 Broadway, Kendall Sq
Cambridge, MA 02142-1093
(617) 494-2051
Fax (617) 494-2370

ENVIRONMENTAL PROTECTION AGENCY
www.epa.gov

Office of Research and Development
ORD/NCER (8722F)
1200 Pennsylvania Ave NW
Washington, DC 20460
(202) 343-9703
Fax (202) 233-0678

NASA
www.nasa.gov

SBIR/STTR Executive Director
Commercial Technology Office,Code RC,NASA-HQ
300 E St SW - Code - XC
Washington, DC 20546
(202) 358-4652
Fax (202) 358-3878

NATIONAL SCIENCE FOUNDATION
www.nsf.gov

Director, Industrial Innovation Programs
SBIR Program
4201 Wilson Blvd, Rm 590
Arlington, VA 22230
(703) 292-7076
Fax (703) 292-9057

Senior Advisor, Industrial Innovation Programs
SBIR Program
4201 Wilson Blvd, Rm 590
Arlington, VA 22230
(703) 292-7069
Fax (703) 292-9057

US SMALL BUSINESS ADMINISTRATION
www.sba.gov

Assistant Administrator, Office of Technology
409 3rd St SW, Mail Code 6540
Washington, DC 20416
(202) 205-7343
Fax (202) 481-5743

SUPPORT CONTRACTORS

BRTRC Inc.
Support Contractor for DOD
8260 Willow Oaks Corp. Dr. Ste 800
Fairfax, VA 22031
(703)204-9277
Fax (703) 204-9447

SECTION 3

MINORITY BUSINESS DEVELOPMENT AGENCY (MBDA)

US Department of Commerce
Minority Business Development Agency Headquarters
1401 Constitution Ave NW
Washington, DC 20230
(888) 324-1551
www.mbda.gov

The Minority Business Development Agency (MBDA) is part of the US Department of Commerce. MBDA is the only federal agency created specifically to foster the establishment and growth of minority-owned businesses in America. MBDA is an entrepreneurially focused and innovative organization committed to wealth creation in minority communities. The Agency's mission is to actively promote the growth and competitiveness of large, medium and small minority business enterprises (MBEs). MBDA actively coordinates and leverages public and private sector resources that facilitate strategic alliances in support of its mission.

Vision Statement
The Minority Business Development Agency is dedicated to becoming an entrepreneurially focused and innovative organization, committed to empowering minority business enterprises for the purpose of wealth creation.

Mission Statement
MBDA's mission is to achieve entrepreneurial parity for MBEs by actively promoting their ability to grow and compete in the global economy. MBDA is addressing challenges faced by MBEs by developing programs that provide the "keys to entrepreneurial success":

- Access to Financing
- Access to the Marketplace
- Access to Education
- Access to Technology

Strategic Direction
The long-term goal of "Achieving entrepreneurial parity for minority business enterprises" is the benchmark by which MBDA's critical Federal government role will be measured. Although businesses with revenues of $1 million or more constitute just 3% of the overall minority business community, these businesses are responsible for 66% of the total revenues of minority-owned enterprises and 54.4% of employment. In order to promote overall U.S. economic growth, it is critical to promote medium to large businesses enterprises that can have a significant impact on employment and the tax base in their communities. Increasing the number of medium and large minority businesses is in the short and long term strategic interest of achieving MBDA's Vision of wealth creation. In pursuit of entrepreneurial parity, MBDA has established a Strategic Growth Policy. The Strategic Growth Policy is designed to address the issue of sustainable business value for firms of size operating in growth industries.

Programs focused on providing access to capital and markets will be the prime components of the Strategic Growth Policy.

A new paradigm for minority business development requires that the public and private sectors expand their present focus from outreach, certification, and dollars spent to include enabling minority business enterprises to achieve size, scale, scope, education, access to technology and capital. Minority business development services must be designed to create sustainable business values. In order to implement the new paradigm, MBDA will develop a more industry focused, data driven technical assistance approach to give minority business owners the tools essential for becoming first or second tier suppliers to corporate America and the Federal government in the new procurement environment. Sustainable value will translate into entrepreneurial parity and strategic growth through increased gross receipts, number of employees, size and scale of firms associated with minority business enterprise.

Programs

MBDA provides funding for a network of Minority Business Development Centers (MBDCs), Native American Business Development Centers (NABDCs), and Business Resource Centers (BRCs) located throughout the Nation. The Centers provide minority entrepreneurs with one-on-one assistance in writing business plans, marketing, management and technical assistance and financial planning to assure adequate financing for business ventures. The Centers are staffed by business specialists who have the knowledge and practical experience needed to run successful and profitable businesses.

MBDA's Portal

MBDA's new Minority Business Internet Portal (website) is an e-commerce solution designed for the MBE community. This Internet platform provides MBEs with access to customized tools and business information to help them grow and thrive in an ever-changing digital economy.

User-driven applications of the Portal (website) include the Phoenix Database of minority-owned firms and the Opportunity Contract Matching System. The Phoenix Database contains descriptive information on MBEs throughout the U.S and is designed to match firms with actual contract opportunities. Individuals will automatically receive E-mail alerts of contractual and international trade opportunities in their area. Purchasers from government and the private sector use Phoenix to identify MBEs that can provide the products and services they need. There is no charge for use of the system.

Other applications of the Portal (website) include the Resource Locator -- a Business Assistance Identifier System; the Business Locator -- a Business-to-Business Matching System; and Match Me to Capital -- a Financier Matching System. The Portal (website) also features a Business Tool Bar for on-line business, business news, success stories, a research library and calendar of events.

MEDWeek

Since 1983, the US President has proclaimed a National MEDWeek observance to recognize the outstanding achievements of MBEs and to honor those corporations and financial institutions that support minority business development. Annual regional conferences and activities are organized by the US Department of Commerce's Minority Business Development Agency (MBDA) in collaboration with the US Small Business Administration's (SBA) Office of Government Contracting and Business Development. These events culminate at the National MED Week Conference in Washington, DC, which provides a unique forum to address the major issues affecting the growth and development of MBEs.

For additional information on MEDWeek, contact MBDA: (888)324-1551 or visit www.medweek.gov

REGIONAL OFFICES of the MINORITY BUSINESS DEVELOPMENT CENTERS NATIVE AMERICAN BUSINESS DEVELOPMENT CENTERS MINORITY BUSINESS OPPORTUNITY COMMITTEES

Minority Business Development Centers are designed to coordinate Federal, State and local business resources to benefit minority business development.
(Note: All addresses and phone numbers are subject to change)

ATLANTA REGION

Alabama - Florida - Georgia - Kentucky- Mississippi - North Carolina - South Carolina - Tennessee - Virgin Islands

Atlanta National Enterprise Center
401 W Peachtree St NW, Ste 1715
Atlanta, GA 30308
(404) 730-3300
Fax (404) 730-3313

Atlanta Regional Enterprise Ctr
51 SW First Ave
Rm 1314, Box 25
Miami, FL 33130
(305) 536-5054
Fax (305) 530-7068

Minority Business Enterprise Centers (MBECs)

Alabama MBEC
450A Government Street
Mobile, AL 36602
(251) 433-2250
Fax (251) 433-2208
www.mbecalabama.org

Georgia Statewide MBEC
760 Spring St NW suite 319
Atlanta, Georgia 30332
(404) 894-2096 -
Fax (404) 894-1192
www.georgiamc.org

Miami/Ft Lauderdale MBEC
3050 Biscayne Blvd, Ste 201
Miami, FL 33137
(786) 316-0888
Fax (786) 316-0090
www.mbdcsouthflorida.org

Miami/Ft Lauderdale MBEC
Satellite Office
3800 West Broward Blvd, Ste 101
Ft Lauderdale, FL 33312
(954) 660-7601
Fax (954) 587-3703
www.mbdcsouthflorida.org

Mississippi MBEC
2318 Pass Road, Ste 4
Biloxi, MS 39531
(228) 385-9324
Fax (228) 385-9328
www.msmbec.org

North Carolina Statewide MBEC
114 West Parrish St, 5th Fl
Durham, NC 27701
(919) 287-3198
Fax(919) 688-8478
www.mbdc-nc.com

South Carolina Statewide MBEC
1515 Richland St Suite C
Columbia, SC 29201
(803) 779-5905 ext 28
Fax (803) 779-5915
www.scmbec.com

Native American Business Enterprise Centers (NABECs)

North Carolina NABEC
719 Old Main Road
Pembroke, NC 28372
(910) 522-1225
Fax (910) 522-5229
www.ncnabec.org

Minority Business Opportunity Committees (MBOCs)

Florida MBOC
6880 Eleanor Dr, Ste 104D
Orlando, FL 32809
(407) 245-6495
Fax (407) 245-6765
www.floridamboc.org

Alabama MBOC
4715 Alton Ct
Birmingham, AL 35210
(205) 957-9779
Fax (205) 957-2114
www.mbocalabama.org

CHICAGO REGION

Illinois - Indiana - Iowa - Kansas - Michigan - Minnesota - Missouri - Nebraska - Ohio - Wisconsin

Chicago National Enterprise Ctr
55 E Monroe St, Ste 2810
Chicago, IL 60603
(312) 353-0182
Fax (312) 353-0191

Minority Business Enterprise Centers (MBECs)

Chicago MBEC
1 East Wacker, Ste 1200
Chicago, IL 60601
(312) 755-8889
Fax (773) 755-8891
www.cmbec.org

Detroit MBEC
3011 West Grand Ave. suite 230
Detroit, MI 48202
(313) 262-7308 ext 103
Fax (313) 262-7342
www.mmbec.com

Indianapolis MBEC
402 West Washington Ste 740
Indianapolis,IN 46204
(317)234-5223
Fax (317) 233-6921
www.idoa.in.gov

St. Louis MBEC
308 N 21st Street suite 740
St Louis MO 63103
(314) 241-6232
Fax (314) 241-1073

Native American Business Development Centers (NABECs)

Minnesota/Iowa NABEC
15542 State Highway 371 NW
Cass Lake, MN 56633
(218) 335-8583 ext 117
Fax (218) 335-8496
www.nabdc.org

Minority Business Opportunity Committees (MBOCs)

Chicago MBOC
1 E Wacker Dr, Ste 1200
Chicago, IL 60601
(312) 755-8887
Fax (312) 755-8891

Milwaukee MBOC
1915 N Martin Luther King Jr Dr
Milwaukee, WI 53203
(414) 372-3773
Fax (414) 372-4005

Indiana MBOC
21 Buffington Harbor Dr suite 182
Gary, IN 46406
(219) 977-7071
Fax (312) 977-9668

DALLAS REGION

Arkansas - Colorado - Louisiana - Montana - New Mexico - North Dakota - Oklahoma - South Dakota - Texas - Utah - Wyoming

Dallas National Enterprise Center
1100 Commerce St room 726
Dallas, TX 75242
(214) 767-8001
Fax (214) 767-0613

Minority Business Enterprise Centers (MBECs)

Dallas/Fort Worth/Arlington MBEC
545 E John carpenter Frwy, Ste 100
Irving, TX 75062
(214) 688-1612
Fax (214) 688-1753

El Paso MBEC
2401 E Missouri
El Paso, TX 79903
(915) 351-6232
Fax (915) 566-9714
www.elpasombec.org

Houston MBEC
4801 Woodway, Ste 210W
Houston, TX 77056
(713) 644-0821
Fax (713) 644-3523

Louisiana MBEC
2714 Canal St, Ste 300
New Orleans, LA 70119
(504) 821-4811
Fax (504) 324-0217
www.louisianambec.com

New Mexico Statewide MBEC
718 Central Ave SW
Albuquerque, NM 87102
(505) 843-7114
Fax (505) 242-2030
www.nm-mbec.com

Oklahoma City MBEC
4205 N Lincoln Blvd, Rm 155
Oklahoma City, OK 73105
(405) 962-1623
Fax (405) 962-1621

San Antonio MBEC
501 W Durango Blvd, Rm 3324
San Antonio, TX 78207-4415
(210) 458-2480
Fax (210) 458-2481
www.sa-mbec.org

Native American Business Enterprise Centers (NABECs)

North/South Dakota NABEC
3315 University Dr, Bldg 61
Bismarck, ND 58504-7596
(701) 530-0668, ext 1359
Fax (701) 530-0607
www.ndsd-nabec.com

NEW YORK REGION

Connecticut - Delaware - Maine - Maryland - Massachusetts - New Hampshire - New Jersey - New York - Pennsylvania - Rhode Island - Puerto Rico - Vermont - Virginia - Washington, DC - West Virginia

New York Nat'l Enterprise Ctr
26 Federal Plaza, Rm 3720
New York, NY 10278
(212) 264-3262
Fax (212) 264-0725

Philadelphia Reg Enterprise Ctr
600 Arch St, Ste 10128
Philadelphia, PA 19106
(215) 861-3597
Fax (215) 861-3595

Boston Regional Enterprise Ctr
One Gateway Center suite 414
Newton, MA 02458
(617) 527-2186
Fax (617) 527-2356

Minority Business Enterprise Centers (MBECs)

Manhattan/Bronx MBEC
14 Penn Plaza, Ste 2007
(225 W 34th St)
New York, NY 10122
(212) 947-5351
Fax (212) 947-1506
www.manhattanmbec.com

New Jersey Statewide MBEC
744 Broad St, Ste 1812
Newark, NJ 07102
(973) 297-1142
Fax (973) 297-1439
www.newjerseymbec.com

Pennsylvania Statewide MBEC
4548 Market St
Philadelphia, PA 19139
(215) 895-4032
Fax (215) 895-4001
www.pa-mbec.com

Puerto Rico Islandwide MBEC
Calle Capitan Espada No 406
Urb El Vedado
Hato Rey, PR 00918
(787) 753-8484
Fax (787) 753-0855
www.mbdcpr.com

Queens MBEC
90-33 160th St
Jamaica, NY 11432
(718) 206-2255
Fax (718) 206-3693
www.jbrc.org

Williamsburg (Brooklyn) MBEC
12 Heyward St
Brooklyn, NY 11211
(718) 522-5620
Fax (718) 522-5931
www.odabdc.org

Washington (DC) Metro MBEC
64 New York Ave NE, Ste 3152
Washington, DC 20002
(202) 671-1885
Fax (202) 671-3073
www.dcmbec.org

Minority Business Opportunity Committees (MBOCs)

Washington, DC MBOC
5203 Leesburg Pike, Ste 605
Falls Church, VA 22041
(703) 575-8437
Fax (703) 575-8407
www.taskpbsi.co

SAN FRANCISCO REGION
Alaska - American Samoa - Arizona - California - Hawaii - Idaho - Nevada - Oregon - Washington

San Francisco Nat'l Enterprise Ctr
221 Main St, Rm 1280
San Francisco, CA 94105
(415) 744-3001
Fax (415) 744-3061

Los Angeles Regional Enterprise Center
Pasadena Office Tower
150 S Los Robles Ave, Ste 460
Pasadena, CA 91101
(626) 768-1015
Fax (626) 768-1020

Minority Business Enterprise Centers (MBECs)

Los Angeles Metro MBEC
3550 Wilshire Blvd, Ste 905
Los Angeles, CA 90010
(213) 368-1450
Fax (213) 368-1454
www.lambdc.org

University of Southern California
2801 South Hoover St
University Park Campus
Los Angeles, CA 90089
(213) 743-5262
Fax (213) 743-4511

Honolulu MBEC
2404 Maile Way, D307
Honolulu, HI 96822
(808) 956-0850
Fax (808) 956-0851
www.honolulu-mbdc.org

Operator Information
Pacific Business Center Program
College of Business Administration
Washington Statewide MBEC
1437 South Jackson St, Ste 320
Seattle, WA 98144
(206) 267-3131
Fax (206) 267-3132
www.mbdcwa.com

Seattle Business Assistance Ctr
1437 South Jackson St, Ste 201
Seattle, WA 98144
(206) 324-4330 x108
Fax (206) 324-4322
www.seattleccd.com

Nevada MBEC
626 S Ninth Street
Las Vegas, NV 89101
(702) 382-9522
(Fax 702) 382-0375

Northern California MBEC
111 N Market Street suite 920
San Jose, CA 95113
(408) 998-8058
Fax (408) 998-8872

Inland Empire MBEC
1825 Chicago Ave suite 130
Riverside, CA 92507
(951) 320-7020
Fax (951) 320-7023
www.inlandempirembec.com

CHARO Community Development Corporation
4301 E Valley Blvd
Los Angeles, CA 90032
(323) 269-0751
Fax (323) 266-4326

Asian Inc.
1167 Mission Street 4th floor
San Francisco, CA 94103
(415) 928-5910
Fax (415) 921-0182
www.asianinc.org

Arizona Statewide MBEC
255 East Osborn Rd, Ste 202
Phoenix, AZ 85012
(602) 248-0007
Fax (602) 279-8900
www.azmbec.org

Arizona Hispanic Chamber of
Commerce Foundation
255 E Osborn Road suite 202
Phoenix, AZ 85012
(602) 279-1800
Fax (602) 279-8900

Native American Business Enterprise Centers (NABECs)

Arizona Statewide NABEC
953 East Juanita Ave
Mesa, AZ 85204
(480) 545-1298 or (480) 545-1412
Fax (480) 545-4208
www.ncaied.org

California Statewide NABEC
11138 Valley Mall, Ste 200
El Monte, CA 91731
(626) 442-3701
Fax (626) 442-7115
www.ncaied.org

Northwest NABEC
3327 NE 125th St, Ste 101
Seattle, WA 98125
(206) 365-7735
Fax (206) 365-7764
www.ncaied.org

Minority Business Opportunity Committees (MBOCs)

Los Angeles MBOC
200 North Spring St 13th floor
Los Angeles, CA 90012
(213) 978-0671
Fax (213) 978-0690
www.lamboc.org

Operator Information
Housing and Economic
Development, City of Los Angeles
200 North Spring Street rm 1303
Los Angeles, CA 90012
(213) 978-3069
Fax(213) 978-0780
www.lamboc.org

SECTION 4

GENERAL SERVICES ADMINISTRATION (GSA)

US General Services Administration (GSA)
1800 F Street NW
Washington, DC 20405
(202) 501-0800
www.gsa.gov

HISTORY

GSA was established on July 1, 1949 by section 101 of the Federal Property and Administrative Services Act as a result of a recommendation by a presidential commission chaired by former President Herbert Hoover. The commission recommended the consolidation of four small agencies into one agency to avoid "senseless duplication, excess cost, and confusion in handling supplies . . . and providing space." Since 1949, GSA has housed federal workers and provided products and services to support the important work of government throughout the country. GSA affects almost $66 billion in financial transactions throughout the government. GSA employs about 14,000 people and has an annual budget of approximately $16 billion.

Mission

GSA helps federal agencies better serve the public by offering, at best value, superior workplaces, expert solutions, acquisition services, and management policies. Creating a Successful Future at GSA by Living Our Values Every Day and Working Together to Achieve Our Goals

Values

- Ethics and integrity in everything we do
- Respect for fellow associates
- Teamwork
- Results orientation
- Professionalism

Goals

- Provide best value for customer agencies and taxpayers
- Achieve responsible asset management
- Operate efficiently and effectively
- Ensure financial accountability
- Maintain a world class workforce and a world class workplace
- Carry out social, environmental, and other responsibilities as a federal agency

GSA Office of Small Business Utilization (OSBU)
1800 F Street NW, Rm 6029
Washington, DC 20405
(202) 501-1021
Fax (202) 208-5938
small.business@gsa.gov

GSA's Office of Small Business Utilization (SBU) advocates for small, minority, veteran, HUBZone, and women business owners. Its mission is to promote increased access to GSA's nationwide procurement opportunities.

SBU monitors and implements small business policies and manages a range of programs required by law. GSA's small business programs nurture entrepreneurial opportunities, open doors to new business horizons, and enhance technological capabilities.

SBU's outreach activities make it possible for the small business community to meet key contracting experts and be counseled on the procurement process. These activities include:

- Procurement networking sessions;
- Marketing strategies and techniques workshops;
- Electronic commerce/electronic data interchange training sessions;
- Interagency networking breakfasts;
- Trade missions;
- Roundtables;
- Workshops for historically black colleges and universities; and
- Procurement conferences.

Business activities are supported by program experts at GSA headquarters, through Small Business Utilization Centers in 11 regional offices, and by the small business technical advisors in the GSA Federal Supply Service, the GSA Federal Technology Service, and the GSA Public Buildings Service.

SBU is responsible for the scope of small business programs mandated by law. Every federal agency is required by the Small Business Act of 1953, as amended by Public Law 95-507, to establish an office that reports to and advises the head of the agency on the implementation functions and duties under this act.

GSA Regions

GSA's 11 geographic regions acquire office space, equipment, supplies, telecommunications, and information technology in support of federal agencies throughout the 50 states, US territories, and overseas.

Region I
(CT, MA, ME, NH, RI, VT)

New England Region Concierge Desk
Thomas P O'Neill, Jr Federal Bldg
10 Causeway St, Rm 900
Boston, MA 02222
(866) 734-1727

Region II
(NJ, NY, PR, VI)

Northeast and Caribbean Region
26 Federal Plaza
New York, NY 10278
(212) 264-3305

Region III
(DE, MD, NJ, PA, VA, WV)

Mid-Atlantic Region
The Strawbridge Bldg
20 N Eighth St
Philadelphia, PA 19107-3191
(215) 446-5100

Region IV
(AL, FL, GA, KY, MS, NC, SC, TN)

Southeast Sunbelt Region
77 Forsyth St, Ste 600
Atlanta , GA 30303
(404) 331-3200
Fax (404) 331-0931

Region V
(IL, IN, MI, MN, OH, WI)

Great Lakes Region
Rm 3700
230 S Dearborn St
Chicago, IL 60604
(312) 353-5395
Fax (312) 353-5595

Region VI
(IA, KS, MO, NE)

Heartland Regional Administrator
1500 E Bannister Rd
Kansas City, MO 64131-3088
(816) 926-7201
Fax (816) 926-7513

Region VII
(AR, LA, NM, OK, TX)

Greater Southwest Region
819 Taylor St
Fort Worth, TX 76102-0000
(817) 978-2321

Region VIII
(CO, MT, ND, SD, UT, WY)

Rocky Mountain Regional Administrator
Denver Federal Center
Bldg 41
Denver, CO 80225-0000
(303) 236-7329

Region IX
(AS, AZ, CA, FE, GU, HI, NV)

Pacific Rim Region
450 Golden Gate Ave
San Francisco , CA 94102
(415) 522-3001

Region X
(AK, ID, OR, WA)

Northwest/Arctic Region
400 15th St SW
Auburn, WA 98001
(253) 931-7000

Region XI
(DC, MD, VA)

NCR Regional Administrator
301 7th St SW
Washington, DC 20407
(202) 708-9100
Fax (202) 708-9966

SECTION 5

DEPARTMENT OF DEFENSE

Department of Defense (DoD)
Office of Small Business Programs (OSBP)
Crystal Gateway North
201 12th St South, Ste 406, West Tower
Arlington, VA 22202
(703) 604-0157
Fax (703) 604-0025
www.acq.osd.mil/OSBP/

Mission to enable the Warfighter to gain access to Small Business' efficiency, innovation and creativity.

Vision to remain an integral player and valued advisor in DoD acquisition strategy development; to remain a leader in innovative initiatives; to grow as a facilitator for accessing untapped resources; and to continue as an advocate for value in DoD procurement.

Programs The Department of Defense (DOD) has numerous programs, which help implement its responsibilities to Small, Small Disadvantaged, Veteran, and Women-Owned businesses

OSBP Offices

Office of the Under Secretary of Defense AT&L
201 12th Street South, Ste 406
Arlington, VA 22202
(703) 604-0157
Fax (703) 604-0025
www.acq.osd.mil/osbp

Office of the Secretary of the Army
106 Army Pentagon Rm 3B514
Washington, DC 20310
(703) 697-2868
Fax (703) 693-3898
www.sellingtoarmy.info

Office of the Secretary of the Navy
720 Kennon St SE
Washington Navy Yard
Bldg 36, Rm 207
Washington, DC 20374-5015
(202) 685-6485
Fax (202) 685-6865
www.hq.navy.mil/osbp

Office of the Secretary of the Air Force
1060 Air Force Pentagon
Washington, DC 20330-1060
(703) 696-1103
Fax (703) 696-1170
www.selltoairforce.org

Defense Information Systems Agency
P O BOX 4502
Arlington VA 22204-4502
(703) 607-6436
Fax (703) 607-4173
www.disa.mil/about/offices/osbp.html

Defense Logistics Agency
8725 John J Kingman Blvd, Ste 2533
Fort Belvoir, VA 22060-6221
(703) 767-1662
Fax (703) 767-9446
www.dla.mil/db

Defense Contract Management Agency
6350 Walker Ln
Alexandria, VA 22032
(877) 662-3960
Fax (703) 428-7776
www.dcma.mil/DCMAHQ/dcma-sb/index.htm

Missile Defense Agency
106 Wynn Drive, Rm 142000
Redstone Arsenal, AL 35898
(256) 955-4828
Fax (256) 312-0435
www.mda.mil/smallbusiness

Defense Intelligence Agency
McDill Blvd, Bldg 6000
Bolling AFB
Washington, DC 20340-0002
(202) 231-2166
Fax (202) 231-2831
www.dia.mil/contracting/osbp.htm

National Geospatial-Intelligence Agency
12310 Sunrise Valley Drive
Reston, VA 20191-3414
(703) 814-4541
www.nga.mil

United States Special Operations Command
7701 Tampa Point Blvd
MacDill Air Force Base
Tampa, FL 33621-5323
(813) 826-9475
www.socom.mil/soal/default.htm

Defense Threat Reduction Agency
8725 John J Kingman Rd
MS 6201
Ft Belvoir, VA 22060-6201
(703) 767-5870
www.dtra.mil/be/business_opp/small/index.cfm

United States Transportation Command
508 Scott Drive
Scott AFB, IL 62225-5357
(618) 256-9619
www.transcom.mil/tccs/OSBP.cfm

Defense Advanced Research Projects Agency
3701 N Fairfax Dr
Arlington, VA 22203-1714
(703) 526-4170
Fax (703) 696-2208
www.darpa.mil/sbpo/small_business.html

Defense Security Cooperation Agency
201 12th Street, Ste 203 East Tower
Arlington, VA 22202
(703) 601-3848
Fax (703) 602-1671
www.dsca.mil/programs/biz-ops/
business_operations.htm

Defense Commisary Agency
DECA Headquarters
1300 East Ave
Fort Lee, VA 23801-1800
(804) 734-8521
Fax (804) 734-8209
www.commissaries.com/business/
small_business.cfm

DOD PROGRAMS

Mentor Protégé Program

The Department of Defense (DoD) Pilot Mentor-Protégé Program seeks to encourage major DoD prime contractors (mentors) to develop the technical and business capabilities of small disadvantaged businesses (SDB's) and other eligible protégés.
(800) 540-8857
www.acq.osd.mil/osbp/mentor_protege/

Small Business Innovation Research (SBIR) Program
Small Business Technology Transfer (STTR) Program

The Department of Defense (DoD) SBIR and STTR programs fund $900 million each year in early-stage R&D projects at small technology companies -- projects that serve a DoD need and have commercial applications.
(866) 724-7457
www.acq.osd.mil/osbp/sbir/index.htm

Indian Incentive Program

The Indian Incentive Program (IIP) is a congressionally sponsored program that provides a 5 percent rebate, on the total amount subcontracted to an Indian-Owned Economic Enterprise or Indian Organization, back to the prime contractor in accordance with FAR 26.1, FAR Clause 52.226-1 and DFAR Clause 252.226-7001. Through the generation of subcontracts to the above-mentioned entities, the IIP fulfills its purpose as an economic multiplier for Native American communities. DoD prime contractors, regardless of size of contract, that contain the above referenced clause(s) are eligible for incentive payments.
(703) 604-0157 ext 181
www.acq.osd.mil/osbp/programs/iip/index.htm

Women-Owned Small Business

The DoD Women-Owned Small Business Program (WOSB) highlights the DoD efforts to achieve the 5% goal for prime and subcontract awards to Small Business concerns owned and controlled by women.
The program objectives are:

- To facilitate, preserve, and strengthen full participation for WOSB concerns in the DoD acquisition programs for goods and services.
- Through programs and activities, including outreach and technical assistance, support the growth of women-owned small business concerns.

(703) 604-0157
www.acq.osd.mil/osbp/programs/wosb/index.htm

HBCU/MI Technical Assistance Program

This office oversees the HBCU/MI programs of the military services and other defense agencies. Their information is also collected and compiled into an annual report that is sent to several Presidential Advisory Boards.
(703) 604-0157
www.acq.osd.mil/osbp/programs/hbcumi/home.htm

Comprehensive Subcontracting Plan Test Program

The DoD Comprehensive Subcontracting Plan Test Program authorizes the negotiation, administration, and reporting of subcontracting plans on a plant, division, or company-wide basis as appropriate. The purpose of the test is to determine whether comprehensive-subcontracting plans will result in increased subcontracting opportunities for Small and Disadvantaged Business while reducing the administrative burdens on contractors.
(703) 604-0157
www.acq.osd.mil/osbp/programs/csp/index.html

DOD Regional Councils

The DOD Regional Councils for Small Business Education and Advocacy are a nationwide network of small business specialists organized to promote the National Small Business Programs of the United States.
(703) 604-0157 ext 180
www.acq.osd.mil/osbp/programs/regional/index.html

Veteran-Owned Small Business Program

The Department of Defense (DoD) has undertaken an aggressive outreach effort to identify small business concerns that are owned and control by veterans and service-disabled veterans. The purpose of the DoD outreach effort is to improve prime and subcontracting opportunities for veteran and service-disabled veteran owned small business concerns. The DoD believes that the sacrifices made by veterans in the service of our country needs to be recognized at all levels of government. Moreover, the Defense Department is committed to make the maximum practicable prime and subcontracting opportunities available to such firms.
(703) 604-0157
www.acq.osd.mil/osbp/programs/veterans/index.html
For other sources of information please contact the Veterans Corp at www.veteranscorp.org

PROCUREMENT TECHNICAL ASSISTANCE CENTERS - PTAC

The Defense Logistics Agency, on behalf of the Secretary of Defense, administers the DoD Procurement Technical Assistance Program (PTAP). PTA Centers are a local resource available that can provide assistance to business firms in marketing products and services to the Federal, state and local governments. www.dla.mil/db/procurem.htm

(Note: All addresses and phone numbers are subject to change)

ALABAMA
PTAC of Alabama
201 Bidgood Hall, University of Alabama
Tuscaloosa, AL 35487
(205) 348-1687
Fax (205) 348-6974
www.al-ptac.org

ALASKA
PTAC of Alaska
430 W 7th Ave, Ste 110
Anchorage, AK 99501-3550
(907) 274-7232
Fax (907) 274-9524
www.ptacalaska.org

ARIZONA
There is no PTAC located in Arizona

ARKANSAS
University of Arkansas Cooperative Extension Service
127 W 5th St
Malvern, AR 72104
(501) 337-5355
Fax (501) 337-5045
www.arcommunities.org/apac.htm

CALIFORNIA
Los Angeles County Office of Small Business
1100 N Eastern Ave, Rm G115
Los Angeles, CA 90063-3200
(323) 881-3964
Fax (323) 881-1871
www.laosb.org

Federal Technology Center
Procurement Assistance Program
4600 Roseville Road, Ste 100
Sacramento, CA 95660
(916) 334-9388 or (866) FTC-PTAC
Fax (916) 334-9078
www.theftc.org/ptac

Riverside Community College District (RCCD)
Corporate Connection
14745 Riverside Dr
Riverside, CA 92518
(951) 571-6472
Fax (951) 653-1051
www.rcchelpsbusiness.com

San Diego Contracting Opportunities Center
4007 Camino Del Rio S, Ste 210
San Diego, CA 92108-4189
(619) 285-7020
Fax (619) 285-7030
www.ptac-sandiego.org

COLORADO
There is no PTAC located in Colorado

CONNECTICUT
Connecticut PTAP
190 Governor Winthrop Blvd,4th Fl
New London, CT 06320
(860) 437-4659 Ext 208
Fax (860) 437-4662
www.ctptap.org

DELAWARE
PTAC of Delaware
One Innovation Way, Ste 301
Newark, DE 19711
(302) 831-0780
Fax (302) 831-0771
www.delawarecontracts.com

DISTRICT OF COLUMBIA
PTAC of Washington DC
One Judiciary Square
441 4th Street NW, Ste 970N
Washington, DC 20001
(202) 256-2705
Fax (202) 724-3786

FLORIDA
University of West Florida
Florida PTAC
401 East Chase St, Ste 100
Pensacola, FL 32502
(850) 473-7806
Fax (850) 473-7813
www.fptac.org

GEORGIA
Georgia Tech Procurement Assistance Center
760 Spring Street NW 3rd floor
Atlanta, GA 30332-0460
(478) 894-0932
Fax (478) 894-0267
www.gtpac.org

GUAM
Guam PTAC
School of Business & Public Administration, Room 116
UOG Station, Mangilao, Guam 96929
(671) 735-2552
Fax (671) 735-5717
www.guamptac.com

HAWAII
Hawaii PTAC (HI-PTAC)
711 Kapiolani Blvd., Ste 1400
Honolulu, HI96813
(808) 594-1895
Fax (808) 594-0255
www.hiptac.org

IDAHO
Idaho Business Network
700 West State St
Boise, ID 83720-0093
(208) 334-2650 Ext 2132
Fax (208) 334-2631
www.cl.idaho.gov

ILLINOIS
Illinois Procurement Technical Assistance Program
620 E Adams St
Springfield, IL 62701
(217) 557-7808
Fax (217) 524-0171
www.ienconnect.com

INDIANA
There is no PTAC located in Indiana.

IOWA
Iowa State University Extension-CIRAS Iowa PTAP
2701 SE Convenience Blvd.,Ste 13
Akeny, IA 50021
(515) 289-0280
Fax (515) 289-0282
www.ciras.iastate.edu/procurement/

KANSAS
PTA Services Provided By:
Missouri Southern State University
Heartland PTAC
3950 E Newman Rd
Joplin, MO 64801-1595
(417) 625-9538
Fax (417) 625-3090
www.heartlandptac.org

KENTUCKY
Kentucky Procurement Assistance Program
500 Mero St
23rd Fl, Capital Plaza Tower
Frankfort, KY 40601
(800) 838-3266
Fax (502) 564-5932
www.thinkkentucky.com/KPAP

LOUISIANA
Louisiana PTAC
635 Cajundome Blvd., Rm 127
Lafayette, LA 70506-4291
(337) 482-6422
Fax (337) 482-5837
www.la-ptac.org

Northwest Louisiana Government procurement center
400 Edwards St
Shreveport, LA 71101
(318) 677-2532
Fax (318) 677-2534
www.mwlagpc.org

MAINE
Maine Procurement Technical Assistance Center
40 Harlow St
Bangor, ME 04401
(207) 942-6389
Fax (207) 942-3548
www.maineptac.org

MARYLAND
Maryland PTAC
7100 Baltimore Ave, Ste 402
College Park, MD 20740-3627
(301) 403-2740 Ext 26
Fax (301) 403-2743
www.mdptap.umd.edu

MASSACHUSETTS
University of Massachusetts-MSBDC/PTAC
227 Isenberg School of Management
Amherst, MA 01003
(413) 545-6303
Fax (413) 545-1273
www.msbdc.org/ptac/rfc.html

MICHIGAN
PTAC of South Central Michigan
One Jackson Square, Ste 1100
Jackson, MI 49201
(517) 788-4680
Fax (517) 782-0061
www.enterprisegroup.org

Southwest Michigan Technical Assistance Center
346 W Michigan Ave
Kalamazoo, MI 49007-3737
(269) 381-2977 Ext 3243
Fax (269) 552-4435
www.ptacsofmichigan.org

Schoolcraft College
18600 Haggerty Rd
Livonia, MI 48152-2696
(734) 462-4438
Fax (734) 462-4673
www.schoolcraft.edu/bdc

Downriver Community Conference PTAC
15100 Northline Rd
Southgate, MI 48105
(734) 362-3477
Fax (734) 281-6661
www.dccwf.org

PTAC Center of NW Michigan
1209 S Garfield Ave
Traverse City, MI 49686
(231) 929-5036
Fax (231) 922-3737
www.nwm.org/ptac.asp

Macomb College PTAC
7900 Tank Ave
Warren, MI 48092
(586) 498-4122
Fax (586) 498-4165
www.ptacsofmichigan.org

Muskegon Area First Procurement Center
380 W Western Ave Ste 202
Muskegon, MI 49440
(231) 722-7700
Fax (231) 722-7251
www.muskegonareafirst.org

Northeast Michigan Consortium
20709 State St
Onaway, MI 49765
(989) 733-8548
Fax (989) 733-8069
www.nemworks.org

MINNESOTA
Metropolitan Economic Development Association
250 S Second Ave, Ste 106
Minneapolis, MN 55401-2214
(612) 259-6565
Fax (612) 317-1002
www.ptac-meda.net

MISSISSIPPI
Mississippi Development Authority
501 N West St
Jackson, MS 39201
(601) 359-3448
Fax (601) 359-5290
www.mississippi.org/mptap

MISSOURI
Missouri PTAC
410 S Sixth St
200 Engineering N
Columbia, MO 65211
(573) 882-3597
Fax (573) 884-4297
www.moptac.net

MONTANA
Big Sky Economic Development Authority
222 North 32 St
Billings, MT 59101-1911
(406) 256-6871
Fax (406) 256-6877
www.bigskyeda-edc.org

NEBRASKA
University of Nebraska at Omaha
NBDC/PTAC
6001 Dodge St, Rm 308
Omaha, NE 68182-0072
(402) 554-6253
Fax (402) 554-6260
http://ptac.unomaha.edu

NEVADA
Nevada Commission of Economic Development
108 E Proctor Street
Carson City, NV 89701
(702) 486-2716
Fax (702) 486-2701
www.nvoutreachcenter.com

NEW HAMPSHIRE
State of New Hampshire
Ofc of Bus & Industrial DoD
PO Box 1856
172 Pembroke Rd
Concord, NH 03302-1856
(603) 271-7581
Fax (603) 271-7583
www.nheconomy.com/ptac.

NEW JERSEY
Foundation At New Jersey Institute of Technology
PTA Center
Fenster Hall Rm 490
Newark, NJ 07102-1982
(973) 596-3105
Fax (973) 596-5501
www.njit.edu/dptac/

Union County Economic Development Corporation
PTA Program
1085 Morris Ave, Ste 531
Library Hall Center
Union, NJ 07083
(908) 527-1166 ext 20
Fax (908) 527-1207
www.ucedc.com

NEW MEXICO
NMSBDC- PTAP
6401 Richards Avenue
Santa Fe, nm 87508
(505) 428-1622
Fax (505) 428-1469

NEW YORK
New York City Dept of Small Business Services
110 William St, 7th Fl
New York, NY 10038
(212) 513-6444
Fax (212) 618-8899
www.nyc.gov

North Country PTAC
1241 Coffeen Street
Watertown, NY 13601
(315) 788-4400
Fax (315) 788-3369
www.northcountryptac.com

Rockland Economic Development Corporation
Two Blue Hill Plaza
PO Box 1575
Pearl River, NY 10965-1575
(845) 735-7040
Fax (845) 735-5736
www.redc.org

South Bronx Overall Economic Development Corporation
SoBRO PTAC
555 Bergen Ave, 3rd Fl
Bronx, NY 10455-1368
(718) 732-7540
Fax (718) 292-6645
www.sobro.org

Cattaraugus County
Department of Economic Development, Planning & Tour
303 Court St
Little Valley, NY 14755
(716) 938-9111 Ext 2331
Fax (716) 938-2779
www.cattco.org

Rochester- County of Monroe Industrial Development Agency (COMIDA)
50 W Main Street suite 8100
Rochester, NY 14614
(585) 753-2015
Fax: (585) 753-2028
www.rochesterptac.com

NORTH CAROLINA
North Carolina PTAC
Small Business & Technology Development Center
5 W Hargett St, Ste 600
Raleigh, NC 27601
(828) 345-1115
Fax (828) 326-9117
www.sbtdc.org/services/gov_procurement.asp

NORTH DAKOTA
There are no PTAC offices located in North Dakota

OHIO

Lawrence Economic Development Corporation
Procurement Outreach Center
216 Collins Ave
P O Box 488
South Point, OH 45680
(740) 377-4550
Fax (740) 377-2091
www.lawrencecountyohio.org

Ohio Department of Development
Procurement Technical Assistance Centers of Ohio
77 South High St, 26th Fl
PO Box 1001
Columbus, OH 43216-1001
(614) 644-1637 or (800)848-1300
Fax (614) 466-4172
www.odod.state.oh.us/dmba/ptac.htm

Mahoning Valley Technical Procurement Center
4319 Belmont Ave
Youngstown, OH 44505-1005
(330) 759-3668 Ext 24
Fax (330) 759-3686
www.mvedc.com

OKLAHOMA

Tribal Government Institute
421 East Comanche, Ste B
Norman, OK 73071
(405) 329-5542
Fax (405) 329-5543
www.tgoik.com

Oklahoma Bid Assistance Network
1500 West Seventh Ave
Stillwater, OK 74074-4364
(405) 743-5592
Fax (405) 743-6821
www.okbid.org

OREGON

The Organization For Economic Initiatives
Government Contract Assistance Program
1144 Gateway Loop, Ste 203
Springfield, OR 97477
(541) 736-1088
Fax (541) 736-1090
www.gcap.org

PENNSYLVANIA

NW Pennsylvania Regional Planning and Development Commission
395 Seneca St
Oil City, PA 16301
(814) 677-4800 Ext 121
Fax (814) 677-7663
www.nwcommission.org

California University of PA
Government Agency Coordination Office
250 University Ave
California, PA 15419
(724) 938-5881
Fax (724) 938-4575
www.cup.edu/advancement/gaco/

Southern Alleghenies Planning and Development Commission
541 58th St
Altoona, PA 16602
(814) 949-6528
Fax (814) 949-6505
www.sapdc.org

Indiana University of Pennsylvania
Government Contracting Assistance Program (GCAP)
5 Robert Shaw, Main Bldg
650 South 13th St
Indiana, PA 15705-1087
(724) 357-7824
Fax (724) 357-3082
www.eberly.iup.edu/gcap/

Johnstown Area Regional Industries
245 Market St suite 200
Johnstown, PA 15901
(814) 535-8675
Fax (814) 535-8677
www.jari.com

Seda Council of Governments
201 Furnace Rd
Lewisburg, PA 17837-8043
(570) 524-4491
Fax (570) 524-9190
www.seda-cog.org/ptac/

Southeast PA PTAC
3819-33 Chestnut Street Ste 325
Philadelphia, PA19104-3238
(215) 746-6472
Fax (215) 573-2135
www.pasbdc.org/

Economic Development Council of Northeast Pennsylvania
Local Development District
1151 Oak St
Pittston, PA 18640
(570) 655-5581 ext 244
Fax (570) 654-5137
www.nepa-alliance.org/ptac

PUERTO RICO

Commonwealth of Puerto Rico
PR Industrial Development Company (PRIDCO)
355 FD Roosevelt Ave
Hato Rey, PR 00914
(787) 758-4747 ext 2234
Fax (787) 751-6239
www.ptacpr.com

RHODE ISLAND

Rhode Island Development Corporation
Business Expansion Division
315 Iron Horse Way suite 101
Providence, RI 02908
(401) 278-9100 ext 175
Fax (401) 273-8270
www.riptac.com

SOUTH CAROLINA

University of South Carolina
SBDC-SC USC Technology Incubator
1225 Laurel Street
Columbia, SC 29201
(803) 777-7877
Fax (803) 777-4403
http://scsbdc.moore.sc.edu/

SOUTH DAKOTA
The University of South Dakota
414 Clark St
Vermillion, SD 57069-2390
(605) 367-5252
Fax (605) 367-5755
www.usd.edu/sdptac

TENNESSEE
Center For Industrial Services
University of Tennessee
193 Polk Ave suite C
Nashville, TN 37210
(615) 532-8885
Fax (615) 532-4937
www.ptactennessee.edu

TEXAS
San Antonio Procurement Technical Assistance Center
100 West Houston
San Antonio, TX 78205
(210) 207-3923
Fax (210) 207-3909
www.sanantonio.gov/edd

Del Mar College-Workforce and Economic Development
3209 S. Staples Rm 146
Corpus Christi, TX 78404
(361) 698-2221
Fax (361) 698-1024
www.delmar.edu/sbdc

Angelina College Procurement Assistance Center
3500 South First Street
Lufkin, TX 75901-7328
(936) 633-5432
Fax (936) 633-5478
www.acpactx.org

Texas Technical University
2579 S Loop 289, Ste 210
Lubbock, TX 79423
(806) 745-1637
Fax (806) 745-6207
www.nwtsbdc.org

El Paso Community College
Contract Opportunities Center
9050 Viscount Bldg B Rm B543
El Paso, TX 79925
(915) 831-7748
Fax (915) 831-7755
www.elpasococ.org

University of Texas At Arlington
Cross Timbers Procurement Ctr
7300 Jack Newell Blvd S
Fort Worth, TX 76118
(817) 272-5978
Fax (817) 272-5992
http://arri.uta.edu/crosstimbers

Panhandle Regional Planning Commission
Economic Development Unit
415 W Eight Ave
Amarillo, TX 79101-2215
(806) 372-3381
Fax (806) 373-3268
www.theprpc.org

University of Houston
2302 Fannin, Ste 200
Houston, TX 79002
713 752-8466
Fax (713) 756-1515
www.sbdc.uh.edu

UTAH
Governors Office of Economic Development (GOED)
Utah PTA Center (UPTAC)
324 South State St, Ste 500
Salt Lake City, UT 84111
(801) 538-8733
Fax (801) 538-8888
http://business.utah.gov/contracting/PTAC

VERMONT
State of Vermont
Dept of Economic Development
National Life Building, Drawer 20
Montpelier, VT 05609
(802) 828-5240
Fax (802) 828-3258
http://economicdevelopment.vermont.gov

VIRGINIA
George Mason University
Mason Enterprise Center
4031 University Dr suite 200
Fairfax, VA 22030
(703) 277-7700
Fax (703) 352-8195
www.vaptap.org

Crater Planning District Commission
Crater Procurement Assistance Center
Po Box 1808
Petersburg, VA 23805
(804) 861-1667
Fax (804) 732-8972
www.craterptac.org

Southwest Virginia Community College
Economic Development Division
724 Community College Rd
Cedar Bluff, VA 24609
(276) 964-7334
Fax (276) 964-7361
www.sw.edu/ptac

WASHINGTON
Economic Development Council of Snohomish County
728 134th St SW suite 128
Everett, WA 98204
(425) 248-4213
Fax (425) 743-5726
www.washingtonptac.org

Native American PTAC
720 Third Ave Ste 1615
Seattle, WA 98104
(206) 816- 6596
Fax (206) 838-3725
www.nativeptac.org

WEST VIRGINIA
Regional Contracting Assistance Center Inc (RCAC)
1116 Smith St, Ste 202
Charleston, WV 25301
(304) 344-2546
Fax (304) 344-2574
www.rcacwv.com

WISCONSIN
Madison Area Technical College Business Procurement Assistance Center
3591 Anderson St, Ste 100
Madison, WI 53704
(608) 243-4490
Fax (608) 243-4486
http://matcmadison.edu/bpac

Wisconsin Procurement Institute, Inc
756 N Milwaukee St
Milwaukee, WI 53202
(414) 270-3600
Fax (414) 270-3610
www.b2gconnect.org

WYOMING
Wyoming PTAC
601 Broadway Ste C
Thermopolis, WY 82443
(307) 921-8499
Fax (307) 864-3747
www.wyomingentrepreneur.biz

DEFENSE CONTRACT MANAGEMENT AGENCY (DCMA) OFFICES

The Defense Contract Management Agency (DCMA) is the Department of Defense (DoD) component that works directly with Defense suppliers to help ensure that DoD, Federal, and allied government supplies and services are delivered on time, at projected cost, and meet all performance requirements. DCMA directly contributes to the military readiness of the United States and its allies, and helps preserve the nation's freedom.

DCMA professionals serve as "information brokers" and in-plant representatives for military, Federal, and allied government buying agencies -- both during the initial stages of the acquisition cycle and throughout the life of the resulting contracts.

(Note: All addresses and phone numbers are subject to change)

ALABAMA

DCMA Birmingham
1910 3rd Avenue N, Rm 201
Birmingham, AL 35203
(205) 716-7402
Fax (205) 716-7403

ARIZONA

DCMA Phoenix
Two Renaissance Sq
40 North Central Ave, Ste 400
Phoenix, AZ 85004-4424
(602) 594-7800
Fax (602) 594-7995/7991

CALIFORNIA

DCMA Boeing Canoga Park
PO Box 7922
6633 Canoga Ave
Canoga Park, CA 91309-7922
(818) 586-4585
Fax (818) 586-7209

DCMA Boeing Space and Communications- Seal Beach
2600 Westminster Blvd
PO Box 3644, Bldg 80, M/S SD32
Seal Beach, CA 90740-7644
(562) 797-3343
Fax (562) 797-2717

DCMA Lockheed Martin Sunnyvale
PO Box 3504, Bldg 154 / Column 2c4
Sunnyvale, CA 94088-3504
(408) 742-5571
Fax (408) 744-0677

DCMA Northern California
700 E Roth Rd, Bldg 330
French Camp, CA 95231-0232
(209) 941-7002
Fax (209) 941-7091

DCMA Northrop Grumman El Segundo
One Hornet Way
El Segundo, CA 90245-2804
(310) 332-2790
Fax (310) 332-2834

DCMA Santa Ana- Ontario
2940 Inland Empire Blvd, Ste 114
Ontario, CA 91764
(909) 944-2124
Fax (909) 944-2187

DCMA Raytheon Los Angeles
2000 E Imperial Hwy
El Segundo, CA 90245-4320
(310) 334-5044
Fax (310) 334-5023

DCMA San Diego
7675 Dagget St, Ste 200
San Diego, CA 92111-2241
(858) 495-7401
Fax (858) 495-7660

DCMA Santa Ana
34 Civic Center Plaza, Rm 813A
Santa Ana, CA 92701-4056
(714) 565-7100
Fax (714) 565-7107

DCMA West
18901 Wilmington Ave Dh-2
Carson, CA 90746-2856

CONNECTICUT

DCMA Hartford
130 Darlin St
East Hartford, CT 06108-3234
(860) 291-7702
Fax (860) 291-7905

DCMA Sikorsky Aircraft
6900 Main St
PO Box 9731
Stratford, CT 06615-9131
(203) 386-6766
Fax (203) 386-6432

FLORIDA

DCMA Lockheed Martin Orlando
5600 Sand Lake Rd, MP 49
Orlando, FL 32819-8907
(407) 356-2401
Fax (407) 356-5166

DCMA Orlando
3555 Maguire Blvd
Orlando, FL 32803-3726
(407) 228-5115
Fax (407) 228-5312

GEORGIA

DCMA Atlanta
2300 Lake Park Dr, Ste 300
Smyrna, GA 30080
(678) 503-6266
Fax (678) 503-6435

DCMA Lockheed Martin Marietta
86 South Cobb Drive, Bldg B-2
Marietta, GA 30063-0260
(770) 494-0084
Fax (770) 494-7883

INDIANA

DCMA Aircraft Propulsion Operations - Rolls Royce Corporation
2001 South Tibbs Ave
Indianapolis, IN 46241-4812
(317) 230-4249
Fax (317) 230-5590

DCMA ITT Northeast Team
P O Box 3700 ITT Mailstop 623A
Fort Wayne, IN 46801-3700

LOUISIANA

DCMA Louisiana/ East Texas
c/o Michoud Assembly Facility
13800 Old Gentilly Rd, Bldg 350
New Orleans, LA 70189-0283
(504) 257-3820
Fax (504) 257-3522

MASSACHUSETTS

DCMA GE Lynn
1000 Western Ave
Lynn, MA 01910-0445
(781) 594-2824
Fax (781) 594-5215

DCMA Boston
495 Summer St
Boston, MA 02210-2138
(617) 753-4006
Fax (617) 753-4005

DCMA Raytheon DCE Center
225 Presidential Way
Woburn, MA 01801

DCMA General Dynamics Pittsfield
100 Plastics Ave
Pittsfield, MA 01201-3696
(413) 494-4001
Fax (413) 494-2686

DCMA Space Seonsors & Communications Operations
50 Apple Hill Dr, M/S T2FR2
Tewksbury, MA 01876
(978) 858-5616
Fax (978) 858-4449

MARYLAND

DCMA Maryland
217 East Redwood St, Ste 1800
Baltimore, MD 21202-5299
(410) 962-9800
Fax (410) 962-3299

DCMA Northrop Grumman Baltimore
7323 Aviation Blvd. Mailstop 1285
Baltimore, MD 21240
(410) 765-6907
Fax (410) 765-3455

MICHIGAN

DCMA Detroit
US Army Tank & Automotive Command (Tacom)
Attn: DCMAW-GJD
Warren, MI 48397-5000
(586) 574-4476
Fax (586) 574-3851

MINNESOTA

DCMA Twin Cities
BH Whipple Federal Bldg, Rm 1150
1 Federal Dr
Ft Snelling, MN 55111
(612) 605-4100
Fax (612) 605-4154

MISSOURI

DCMA Boeing St Louis
PO Box 516, MC S598-1521
St Louis, MO 63166-0516

NEW JERSEY

DCMA Lockheed Martin Deleware Valley
1 Federal Street Mailstop AE-2-W
Moorestown, NJ 08102-1013

DCMA Springfield
Bldg 1, ARDEC
Picatinny, NJ 07806-5000
(973) 724-8304
Fax (973) 724-5791

NEW YORK

DCMA Aircraft Integrated Maintenance Operations - Bethpage
600 Grumman Rd W, M/S D23-025
Bethpage, NY 11714-3582
(516) 575-2447
Fax (516) 346-9253

DCMA Lockheed Martin Systems Integration - Owego
1801 State Rte 17C
Owego, NY 13827-3998
(607) 751-5264
Fax (607) 751-5333

DCMA Long Island
605 Stewart Ave
Garden City, NY 11530-4761
(516) 228-5715
Fax (516) 228-5938

DCMA NSSO Lockheed Martin
55 Charles Lindberg Blvd.
Mitchel Field, NY 11553-3682

DCMA Syracuse
615 Erie Blvd West, Ste 300
Syracuse, NY 13204-2408
(315) 423-8594
Fax (315) 423-8960

OHIO

DCMA GE Aircraft Engines-Cincinnati
1 Neumann Way
Mail Drop N-1
Cincinnati, OH 45215-6303
(513) 243-6015
Fax (513) 243-7615

DCMA Cleveland
Admiral Kidd Ctr
555 East 88th St
Bratenahl, OH 44108-1068
(216) 681-1524
Fax (216) 681-1588

DCMA Dayton
Area C, Building 30
1725 Van Patton Dr
Wright-Patterson AFB, OH 45433-5302
(937) 656-3072
Fax (937) 656-1474

DCMA Lockheed Martin Team
1210 Massillon Road
Akron, OH 44315-0001

PENNSYLVANIA

DCMA Boeing Philadelphia
PO Box 16859, MS P23-50
Philadelphia, PA 19142-0895
(610) 591-8500
Fax (610) 591-2234

DCMA Philadelphia
700 Robbins Ave, Bldg 4-A
PO Box 11427
Philadelphia, PA 19111-0427
(215) 737-3402
Fax (215) 737-7353

RHODE ISLAND

DCMA NSSO Portsmouth
1847 West Main Road
Portsmouth, RI 02871-1087

TEXAS

DCMA AIMO Nort Texas
Greenville, TX 75402-3234

DCMA Dallas
600 South Pearl St, Ste 1630
Dallas, TX 75201-2843
(214) 744-4581
Fax (214) 670-9293

VIRGINIA

DCMA Procurement Center
6350 Walker Lane Ste 200
Alexandria, VA 22310-3241
(703) 428-1700
Fax (703) 428-1835

DCMA OCT Specialty Metals Office
6350 Walker Ln, Rm 300
Alexandria, VA 22310
(703) 428-1901
Fax (703) 428-1948

DCMA Southern Virginia
190 Bernard Rd, Bldg 117
Fort Monroe, VA 23651
(757) 788-4854
Fax (757) 788-3281

VERMONT

DCMA General Dynamics
Armament Sys Team
128 Lakeside Ave
Burlington, VT 05401-4985
(414) 494-4001
Fax (414) 494-2686

SECTION 6

DEPARTMENT OF TRANSPORTATION

Department of Transportation (DOT)
Office of Small & Disadvantaged Business Utilization (OSDBU)
1200 New Jersey Avenue SE, W56-485
Washington, DC 20590
(202) 366-1930
Fax (202)366-7228
www.osdbu.dot.gov

The Department of Transportation policy of assisting small businesses owned and controlled by socially and economically disadvantaged individuals, including minorities and women, in participating in contracting opportunities created by DOT financial assistance programs.

Background

The US Department of Transportation's (DOT) Disadvantaged Business Enterprise (DBE) Program was developed to help small businesses owned and controlled by socially and economically disadvantaged individuals, including minorities and women, to participate in contracting opportunities created by DOT financial assistance programs. The DBE program applies to projects funded at the state and local level as well as federal efforts; therefore, a business needs to be aware that state and local governments may have other types of certifications with different requirements. The US DOT distributes over $20 billion annually for highway, transit, and airport improvement projects across the nation.

To ensure that all Americans have a fair chance to participate in these transportation contracts, Congress enacted the first Disadvantaged Business Enterprise (DBE) statutory provision in 1983. In 1987, Congress reauthorized the legislation. Among other changes, the program was extended to airports and women were added to the groups presumed to be disadvantaged. The program was continued in 1991 with the Intermodal Surface Transportation Efficiency Act (ISTEA) and then again in 1998 with the Transportation Equity Act for the 21st Century (TEA-21).

Primarily, three major DOT operating administrations are involved in the DBE program: the Federal Highway Administration (FHWA), Federal Aviation Administration (FAA), and Federal Transit Administration (FTA).

The DOT DBE program is carried out by state and local transportation agencies under the rules and guidelines in the Code of Federal Regulations Title 49 part 26.

DBEs are certified by the primary recipients of federal transportation assistance, i.e., state and local transportation agencies. These recipients establish goals for the participation of disadvantaged entrepreneurs and certify the eligibility of DBE firms to participate in their DOT-assisted contracts.

Unlike the SBA programs, DBE firms are subject to on-site reviews before a certification can be granted. They also must comply with state and local procurement rules and regulations.

Final Rule Provisions

This final rule revises the Department of Transportation's regulations for its disadvantaged business enterprise (DBE) program. The DBE program is intended to remedy past and current discrimination against disadvantaged business enterprises, ensure a level playing field and foster equal opportunity in DOT-assisted contracts, improve the flexibility and efficiency of the DBE program, and reduce burdens on small businesses. This final rule replaces the former DBE regulation, which now contains only the rules for the separate DBE program for airport concessions, with a new regulation. The new regulation reflects President Clinton's policy to mend, not end, affirmative action programs. It modifies the Department's DBE program in light of developments in case law requiring narrow tailoring of such programs and last year's Congressional debate concerning the continuation of the DBE program. It responds to comments on the Department's December 1992 notice of proposed rulemaking (NPRM) and its May 1997 supplemental notice of proposed rulemaking (SNPRM).

SMALL BUSINESS SPECIALISTS HEADQUARTERS

Each Operating Administration in the Department of Transportation has Small Business Specialists devoted to providing procurement information to small businesses and to act as their advocates in the contracting arena.

Federal Aviation Administration (FAA)
800 Independence Ave SW
Washington, DC 20591
(866) TELL-FAA or (866) 835-5322

Federal Highway Administration (FHWA)
Headquarters- Southeast Federal Center Building
1200 New Jersey Ave. SE
Washington, DC 20590-9898
(202) 366-2346

Federal Motor Carrier Safety Administration (FMCSA)
1200 New Jersey Ave. SE, Ste W60-300
Washington, DC 20590
(800) 832-5660

Federal Railroad Administration (FRA)
Associate Administrator for Safety
1200 New Jersey Ave. SE
Washington, DC 20590
(202) 493-6300

Federal Transit Administration (FTA)
Office of Progam Management
1200 New Jersey Ave SE
Washington, DC 20590
(202) 366-4043

Maritime Administration (MARAD)
1200 New Jersey Ave SE
Washington, DC 20590
(800) 99-MARAD or (800) 996-2723

National Highway Traffic Safety Administration (NHTSA)
1200 New Jersey Ave SE , West Building
Washington, DC 20590
(888) 327-4236

Office of the Secretary (OST)
1200 New Jersey Ave SE
Washington, DC 20590
(202) 366-4000

Office of the Inspector General
1200 New Jersey Ave SE 7th Fl
Washington, DC 20590
(202) 366-1959

Saint Lawrence Seaway Development Corporation (SLSDC)
Policy Headquarters
1200 New Jersey Ave SE, Ste W32-300
Washington, DC 20590
(800) 758-2779 or (202) 366-0091

Operations Headquarters
180 Andrews Street
Massena, NY 13662
(315) 764-3200

DISADVANTAGED BUSINESS ENTERPRISE (DBE) LIAISON & CERTIFICATION OFFICES

ALABAMA
DBE Coordinator
2720 Gunter Park Dr W
Montgomery, AL 36109-3050
(334) 244-6261
Fax (334) 260-5313

Compliance Manager
1409 Coliseum Blvd
Montgomery, AL 36130-3050
(334) 242-6340
Fax (334) 263-7586

ALASKA
Manager, Civil Rights Office
Supervisor, DBE Certification
Department of Transportation
2200 E 42nd Ave
PO Box 196900
Anchorage, AK 99519-6900
(907) 269-0851
Fax (907) 269-0847

ARIZONA
Civil Rights Administrator
DBE Certification Program Manager
Department of Transportation
1135 N 22nd Ave, 2nd Fl
Phoenix, AZ 85009
(602) 712-7761
Fax (602) 712-8429

ARKANSAS
Section Head EEO/DBE
State Hwy & Transportation Dept
PO Box 2261
Little Rock, AR 72203
(501) 569-2298
Fax (501) 569-2693

CALIFORNIA
Deputy Director
Chief, Office of Certification
Civil Rights Program, MS-79
CALTRANS
1823 14th St
Sacramento, CA 95811
(866) 810-6346
Fax (916) 324-1949

COLORADO
Supervisor, DBE Certification
Department of Transportation
4201 E Arkansas Ave
Denver, CO 80222
(303) 757-9599
Fax (303) 512-4146

CONNECTICUT
Director, Office of Equal Opportunity Assurance
Manager, Division of Control Compliance
Department of Transportation
2800 Berlin Turnpike, Rm 1314
Newington, CT 06131-7546
(860) 594-3067 or (860) 594-2169
Fax (860) 594-3016

DELAWARE
DBE Program Manager
Department of Transportation
PO Box 778, 800 Bay Road
Dover, DE 19901
(302) 760-2035
Fax (302) 739-2254

DISTRICT OF COLUMBIA
Office of Integrity & Workforce Relations
DoT -- Civil Rights Division
2000 14th St NW, 5th Fl
Washington, DC 20009
(202) 671-2806
Fax (202) 671-2355

FLORIDA
DBE Certification Manager
Department of Transportation - EEO
605 Suwannee St
Tallahassee, FL 32399-0450
(850) 414-4747
Fax (850) 488-3914

GEORGIA
DBE EEO Division Director
Department of Transportation
One Georgia Center
600 West Peachtree Street NW, 7th FL
Atlanta, GA 30308
(404) 631-1972 or 631-1289
Fax (404) 631-1943

HAWAII
DBE Program Supervisor
Department of Transportation
869 Punchbowl St, Rm 112
Honolulu, Hawaii 96813
(808) 587-2023
Fax (808) 587-2025

IDAHO
EEO Contract Compliance Officer
Transportation Department
PO Box 7129
Boise, ID 83707-1129
(208) 334-8458
Fax (208) 332-7812

DBE Supportive Services Coordinator
Transportation Department
PO Box 7129
Boise, ID 83707-1129
(208) 334-8567
Fax (208) 332-7812

ILLINOIS
Bureau Chief
Small Business Enterprises
Department of Transportation
2300 South Dirksen Pkwy, Rm 319
Springfield, IL 62764
(217) 785-5947
Fax (217) 785-1524

Office of Business & Work Diversity
Director
2300 S. Dirksen Parkway room 300
Springfield IL 62764
(217) 785-5395
Fax (217) 785-8417

INDIANA
Director, Economic Opportunity Division
100 North Senate Avenue, Room N750
Indianapolis, IN 46204
(317) 232-5328
Fax (317) 233-0891

IOWA
Contracts Engineer
Department of Transportation
800 Lincoln Way
Ames, IA 50010
(515) 239-1414
Fax (515) 239-1325

KANSAS
Civil Rights Administration
Department of Transportation
Eisenhower State Office Building
700 Southwest, Suite 350
Topeka, KS 66612
(785) 296-7940
Fax (785) 296-0723

KENTUCKY
DBE Branch Manager
Kentucky Transportation Cabinet
200 Mero St
Frankfort, KY 40622
(502) 564-3601 ext 3042
Fax (502) 564-1491 or (502) 564-2114

LOUISIANA
Compliance Programs Director
DBE Certification Manager
Department of Transportation & Development
PO Box 94245
Baton Rouge, LA 70804-9245
(225) 379-1382 or (225) 379-1762
Fax (225) 379-1865

MAINE
Civil Rights Office
Department of Transportation
#16 State House Station
Augusta, ME 04333
(207) 624-3066
Fax (207) 624-3041

MARYLAND
Director
Office of Minority Businesses Enterprises
Department of Transportation
7201 Corporate Center
Hanover, MD 21706
(410) 865-1240
Fax (410) 865-1309

MASSACHUSETTS
Director of Legal and Regulatory Compliance; State Office of Minority and Women Business Assistance (SOMWBA)
10 Park Plaza, Rm 3740
Boston, MA 02116
(617) 973-8692
Fax (617) 973-8637

MICHIGAN
EEO Office
Department of Transportation
PO Box 30050
Lansing, MI 48909
(517) 373-2377
Fax (517) 335-0945

MINNESOTA
Office of Civil Rights
Department of Transportation
395 John Ireland Blvd, MS 170
St Paul, MN 55155
(651) 366-3073
Fax (651) 366-3129

Director, Chair of the Unified Certification Program Metropolitan Council
390 Robert Street North
St Paul, MN 55101-1805
(651) 602-1085

MISSISSIPPI
DBE Coordinator
Department of Transportation
Office of Civil Rights
PO Box 1850
Jackson, MS 39215-1850
(601) 359-7466
Fax (601) 576-4504

MISSOURI
External Civil Rights Administration
Hwy & Dept of Transportation
PO Box 270
1617 Missouri Blvd.
Jefferson City, MO 65102
(573) 751-2859
Fax (573) 526-5640

MONTANA
Chief, Civil Rights Bureau
Department of Transportation
2701 Prospect Ave
PO Box 201001
Helena, MT 59620-1001
(406) 444-6335
Fax (406) 444-7685

DBE Program Manager
Department of Transportation
2701 Prospect Ave
PO Box 201001
Helena, MT 59620-1001
(406) 444-6337
Fax (406) 444-7685

NEBRASKA
Highway Civil Rights Coordinator
PO Box 94759
Lincoln, NE 68509-4791
(402) 479-4531
Fax (402) 479-3728

NEVADA
Contract Compliance Manager, DBE Program
Department of Transportation
1263 South Stewart St
Carson City, NV 89712-0002
(775) 888-7497
Fax (775) 888-7235

NEW HAMPSHIRE
DBE Coordinator
Department of Transportation
7 Hazen Dr
Concord, NH 03302
(603) 271-6612
Fax (603) 271-8817

NEW JERSEY
Division of Civil Rights/Affirmative Action
Department of Transportation
PO Box 600
Trenton, NJ 08625-0600
(609) 530-4735
Fax (609) 530-4030

NEW MEXICO
Chief, EEO Program Bureau
Hwy & Transportation Department
1596 Pacheco Aspen Plaza, Ste 107
Santa Fe, NM 87505
(505) 827-1774
Fax (505) 827-1779

DBE Certification
Hwy & Transportation Department
1596 Pacheco Aspen Plaza, Ste 107
Santa Fe, NM 87505
(505) 827-1776
Fax (505) 827-1779

NEW YORK
Director, Civil Rights Bureau
Office of Audit & Risk Management
50 Wolf Road 6th floor
Albany, NY 12232-0444
(518) 457-1129
Fax (518) 458-5517

Certification Supervisor of DBE,
Contract Audit Bureau
Office of Audit & Risk Management
50 Wolf Road 1st floor
Albany, NY 12232-0444
(518) 457-3180
Fax (518) 457-1675

NORTH CAROLINA
Director,Opportunity and Workforce
Development
Department of Transportation
104 Fayetteville Street
Raleigh, NC 27601
(919) 508-1798
Fax (919) 508-1814

Manager, Unified Certification
Program, Contractural Services Unit
Department of Transportation
1 S. Wilmington Street
Raleigh, NC 27601
(919) 733-5616 ext 334
Fax (919) 715-3584

NORTH DAKOTA
Director, Civil Rights Division
Department of Transportation
608 East Blvd Ave
Bismarck, ND 58505-0700
(701) 328-2576
Fax (701) 328-1965

OHIO
Manager External Civil Rights
Office of Contracts
Department of Transportation
1980 W Broad St
Columbus, Ohio 43223
(614) 466-7699
Fax (614) 728-2078

OKLAHOMA
Transportation Manager
Regulatory Services Division
Department of Transportation
200 NE 21st St
Oklahoma City, OK 73105
(405) 521-6046
Fax (405) 522-2136

OREGON
Small Business Program Manager
Office of Civil Rights
Department of Transportation
355 Capitol St NE
Salem, OR 97301-3781
(503) 986-4355
Fax (503) 986-6382

PENNSYLVANIA
Director, Bureau of Equal Opportunity
Department of Transportation
Keystone Building
400 North St, 5th Fl
Harrisburg, PA 17120
(717) 787-5891 or (800) 468-4201
Fax (717) 772-4026

DBE Investigator Incharge
Department of Transportation
Office of the Chief Counsel
Commonwelth Keystone Bldg
400 N St, 9th Fl
Harrisburg, PA 17120-0096
(717) 787-7014
Fax (717) 772-7241

PUERTO RICO
DBE Coordinator, Civil Rights Office
Department of Transportation &
Public Works
Highway & Transportation Authority
PO Box 42007
San Juan, PR 00940-2007
(787) 729-1562
Fax (787) 721-2621

RHODE ISLAND
Office of Administrative Services
Department of Transportation
2 Capitol Hill, Rm 111
Providence, RI 02903
(401) 222-1717
Fax (401) 222-1086

SOUTH CAROLINA
Director, DBE Program Development
Department of Transportation
955 Park St, Rm117
Columbia, SC 29202-0191
(803) 737-1372
Fax (803) 737-2021

Director, Business Development and
Special Programs
DBE Program Development
Department of Transportation
955 Park St, P O Box 191
Columbia, SC 29202
(803) 737-1717
Fax (803) 737-1086

SOUTH DAKOTA
DBE Liason Officer
Becker-Hanen Building
700 E. Broadway Ave
Pierre, SD 57501
(605) 773-4906
Fax (605) 773-2893

TENNESSEE
Director, Small Business Development
DBE Program
James K Polk Bldg, Ste 1800
Nashville, TN 37243
(615) 741-3681
Fax (615) 741-3169

Executive Director, Civil Rights Office
Department of Transportation
505 Deaderick Street, Ste 1800
Nashville, TN 37243
(615) 741-3681 or (888) 370-3647
Fax (615)741-3169

TEXAS
Director, Office of Civil Rights
Department of Transportation
200 E Riverside Drive, 2nd Fl
Austin, TX 78704-1259
(512) 486-5500 or (512) 486-4700
Fax (512) 416-4711 or (512) 486-5509

UTAH
Civil Rights Manager
DOT-Civil Rights Section
4501 South 2700 West
Salt Lake City, UT 84114-1200
(801) 965-4695
Fax (801) 965-4101

DBE Certification Officer
DOT-Civil Rights Section
4501 South 2700 West
Salt Lake City, UT 84114-1200
(801) 965-4100
Fax (801) 965-4101

VERMONT
Office of Civil Rights and Chief Labor Compliance
Department of Transportation
1 National Life Drive
Montpelier, VT 05633-5001
(802) 828-5561
Fax (802) 828-1047

DBE Program Manager
Office of Civil Rights and Labor Compliance
Department of Transportation
1 National Life Drive
Montpelier, VT 05633-5001
(802) 828-2715
Fax (802) 828-1047

VIRGIN ISLANDS
Civil Rights Program Manager
Department of Transportation & Public Works
6002 Croix, USVI 00820-4428
(340) 773-1290 x2292

VIRGINIA
Chief of Equal Business Opportunity
1401 East Broad Street
Richmond, VA 23219
(804) 786-2085

Manager, VA Department of Minority Business Enterprise
1111 East Main Street, suite 300
Richmond, VA 23219
(804) 786-8973

WASHINGTON
Director, Office of Equal Opportunity
Department of Transportation
310 Maple Park Ave SE
Olympia, WA 98504-7314
(360) 705-7090
Fax (360) 705-6801

Certification Manager
Office of Minority & Women's Business Enterprises
Department of Transportation
406 S Water St
Olympia, WA 98504
(360) 704-1197 ext 107
Fax (360) 586-7079

WEST VIRGINIA
EEO Division, DBE Program Manager
West Virginia Division of Highways
1900 Kanawha Blvd E, Bldg 5, Rm 948
Charleston, WV 25305-0430
(304) 558-3931
Fax (304) 558-4236

WISCONSIN
Civil Rights & Compliance Manager
Department of Transportation
4802 Sheboygan Ave
PO Box 7965, Rm 451
Madison, WI 53707
(608) 264-6669
Fax (608) 267-3641

WYOMING
DBE/ Contract Compliance Officer
Department of Transportation
5300 Bishop Blvd
Cheyenne, WY 82009-3340
(307) 777-4457
Fax (307) 777-4765

SECTION 7

DEPARTMENT OF THE TREASURY

Department of the Treasury
Treasury Office of Small & Disadvantaged Business Utilization
1500 Pennsylvania Avenue, NW
Washington, DC 20220
(202) 622-2000
Fax (202) 622-6415
www.treas.gov/offices/management/dcfo/osdbu/

The Office of Small Business Development (OSBD) is responsible for the development and implementation of an effective program of activities directed at ensuring small, HUBZone small, small disadvantaged, women-owned small, veteran owned small, and service disabled veteran owned small business participation in the Department's direct procurement and subcontract opportunities.

The OSBD monitors all Department of the Treasury procurement activities that involve the participation of small business concerns, including the goal setting and procurement practices of all Treasury bureaus. It also negotiates prime and subcontract procurement goals with the Small Business Administration. Mediating and resolving sensitive procurement related issues are also a function of the OSBD. It also is responsible for implementing Treasury's Mentor-Protégé Program, Success Partnerships.

The OSBD serves an important function in assisting firms in their marketing of the Department and all of the bureaus. To this end, the OSBD sponsors a monthly Vendor Outreach Session to enable small businesses to meet the bureau small business specialists and discuss upcoming procurement opportunities. The OSBD also oversees the planning and management of the annual OSDBU Directors Procurement Conference held each Spring to assist firms in marketing their companies to both procurement and program officials.

Small Business Specialists

Comptroller of the Currency
250 E St SW, AQS 4-13
Washington, DC 20219
(202) 874-5442
Fax (202) 874-5625

Headquarters Operations
1500 Pennsylvania Ave NW
MS: 1425 New York Avenue NW, Ste 2100
Washington, DC 20220
(202) 622-2709
Fax (202) 622-2343

Bureau of Engraving & Printing
14th & C Sts SW, Rm 705A
Washington, DC 20228
(202) 874-5827
Fax (202) 874-2200

Financial Crime Enforcement Network
2070 Chain Bridge Rd
Vienna, VA 22027
(703) 905-5154
Fax (703) 905-3684

Financial Management Service
401 14th St SW, Rm 457F
Washington, DC 20227
(202) 874-0863
Fax (202) 874-7275

Internal Revenue Service
Constellation Centre
6009 Oxon Hill Rd, 5th Fl
Oxon Hill, MD 20745
(202) 283-1350
Fax (202) 283-1528

IRS Northeast Area Field Office
290 Broadway
New York, NY 10007-1867
(212) 436-1481 or (212) 436-1776
Fax (212) 436-1849

IRS Southeast Area Field Office
2888 Woodcock Blvd, Ste 300
Atlanta, GA 30341
(404) 338-9204
Fax (404) 338-9203

IRS Mid-States Area Field Office
4050 Alpha Rd, MSRO 1800
Dallas, TX 75244-4203
(972) 308-1637 or (972) 308-1988
Fax (972) 308-1928

IRS Western Area Field Office
333 Market St, Ste 1400
San Francisco, CA 94105
(415) 848-4735
Fax (415) 848-4711

IRS Martinsburg Computing Center
250 Murall Dr, MS-223
Kearneysville, WV 25430
(304) 264-5589
Fax (304) 264-7008

US Mint
801 Ninth St NW
Washington, DC 20220
(202) 354-7823
Fax (202) 756-6162

Bureau of the Public Debt
200 3rd St, Avery 5 - F
Parkersburg, WV 26106-1328
(304) 480-7291 or (304) 480-7141
Fax (304) 480-7203

Alcohol & Tobacco Tax and Trade Bureau
1310 G St NW, Ste 300E
Washington, DC 20552
(202) 927-0950
Fax (202) 435-7425

Office of Thrift Supervision
1700 G St NW, 3rd Fl
Washington, DC 20552
(202) 906-7624
Fax (202) 906-5648

SECTION 8

DEPARTMENT OF VETERANS AFFAIRS

Department of Veterans Affairs (VA)
Office of Small Disadvantaged Business Utilization (OSDBU)
810 Vermont Avenue, NW
Washington, DC 20420
Telephone: (202) 461-4300
FAX: (202) 461-4301
Toll Free: (800) 949-8387
E-Mail: OSDBU@va.gov
www.va.gov/OSDBU/index.asp

The Office of Small and Disadvantaged Business Utilization (OSDBU) serves as the Department of Veterans Affairs (VA) advocate, to assist and support the interests of small businesses. A related mission of this office is to provide outreach and liaison support to businesses (large and small) and other members of the private sector concerning acquisition related issues. In addition, the office is responsible for monitoring VA implementation and execution of the socioeconomic procurement programs.

Mission

The mission of the OSDBU is to advocate for the maximum practicable participation of small, small disadvantaged, veteran-owned, women-owned and empowerment zone businesses in contracts awarded by the Department of Veterans Affairs and in subcontracts which are awarded by VA's prime contractors.

Functions and Activities

OSDBU is responsible for the development of Department-wide policies, programs and practices relating to small business concerns, including:

- Educating and training VA staff;
- Negotiating prime and subcontracting goals with contracting activities;
- Monitoring achievements and managing information system reports to VA executives;
- Advising contracting officials on procurement strategies to ensure equitable opportunities for small business concerns;
- Conducting market research to identify small business sources for competitive actions;
- Reviewing and approving procurements to assist concerns in SBA's special business development program. As the small business advocates for the Department,
- OSDBU staff: Train, counsel and assist small businesses in their understanding of federal and agency procurement procedures.
- Advise businesses on marketing their products and services to VA and other federal agencies.
- Serve as the liaison office when small businesses encounter payment problems or other difficulties in working with VA offices.

Center for Veterans Enterprise (CVE)

810 Vermont Avenue, N. W.
Washington, D.C. 20420
Toll Free: (866) 584-2344 or (202) 303-3260
FAX (202) 254-0238
E-Mail: VACVE@va.gov
Web Site: http://www.vetbiz.gov

The Department of Veterans Affairs created the Center for Veterans Enterprise (CVE), which is solely dedicated to assisting veterans in starting and building businesses. They maintain a web site that serves as the federal government portal for veteran-owned businesses known as VETBIZ.GOV

Register in the Veteran Information Pages (VIP) at http://www.vip.vetbiz.gov for:
Special consideration for federal contracting opportunities from prime contractors and federal government agencies, notices of contracting opportunities, and information and news affecting Veteran-Owned and Service-Disabled businesses.

CVE's website provides many links to sites providing assistance to veterans entrepreneurs, such as the Small Business Administration's (SBA) Veteran's Business Development, Officers located in local SBA offices throughout the nation, and the National Association of State Directors of Veterans Affairs (NASDVA), for information on state assistance to veterans.

Office of Veterans Business Development
U.S. Small Business Administration Veterans Business Outreach Program

Mission-

The mission of the Office of Veterans Business Development is to maximize the availability, applicability and usability of all administration small business programs for Veterans, Service-Disabled Veterans, Reserve Component Memebers, and their Dependents or Survivors

Veterans Business Outreach Program

The Veterans Business Outreach Program (VBOP) is designed to provide entrepreneurial development services such as business training, counseling and mentoring, and referralsfor eligible veterans owning or considering starting a small business. The SBA has four organizations participating in this cooperative agreement and serving ass Veterans Business Outreach Centers (VBOC).

Veterans Business Outreach Centers:

Massachusetts District Office
Northeast Veterans Business Resource Center
360 Merrimack Street, Bldg 9, Ste 209
Lawrence, MA 01843
(617) 938-3933
Fax (617) 507-7799
States covered- Massachusetts, Maine, Vermont, Rhode Island, Connecticut, New Hampshire

Syracuse District Office
The Research Foundation of the State University of New York SUNY @ Farmingdale
350 Broadhollow Road, Campus Commons
Farmingdale, NY 11735
(800) 732-7232
Fax (631) 370-8895

States covered- New York, New Jersey, Puerto Rico, Virgin Islands
Pittsburgh District Office
Robert Morris University
600 Fifth Avenue
Pittsburgh, PA 15219
(412) 397-6842
Fax (412) 227-6850
States covered- Pennsylvania, Maryland, Virginia, West Virgina, Delaware, District of Columbia

Michigan District Office
VetBiz Central,Inc.
711 N Saginaw Street, Ste 206
Flint, MI 48503
(810) 767-8387
Fax (810) 767-8662
States covered-Michigan, Minnesota, Wisconsin, Illinois, Ohio, Indiana

Lower Rio Grande Valley District Office
The University of Texas- Pan American
1201West University Drive
Edinburg, TX 78539
(956) 292- 7547
Fax (956) 292-7561
States covered- Texas, New Mexico, Arkansas, Louisiana, Oklahoma

St.Louis District Office
Veterans Advocacy Foundation, Inc.
4236 Lindell Blvd., Ste 102
Saint Louis, MO 63108
(314) 531-8387
Fax (877) 825-4190
States covered- Missouri, Kansas, Iowa, Nebraska

Jacksonville Florida District Office
The University of West Florida in Pensacola
2500 Minnesota Avenue
Lynn Haven, FL 32444
(850) 271-1108 or (800) 542-7232
Fax (850) 271-1109
States covered-Florida, Georgia, Alabama, South Carolina, Mississippi, Kentucky, Tennessee, North Carolina

SECTION 9

FEDERAL SMALL DISADVANTAGED/WOMEN-OWNED BUSINESS UTILIZATION/COMPLIANCE

Public Law 104-106, the Federal Acquisition Reform Act of 1996, made significant changes in federal procurement policies (see Legislation Section 1, PL 104-106). These changes will be reflected by new and/or amended Federal Acquisition Regulations (FAR).

In June a final Rule was issued to bring the FAR into conformance with revised small business size standards. Many other changes were made in this same Rule which impact small and small/disadvantaged businesses. A proposed Rule was issued by the Federal Acquisition Regulatory Council in fall, 1996, to amend federal regulations which facilitate contracting by electronic commerce.

Public Law 95-507 mandates that all prime contracts issued by Federal Agencies to large businesses which are over $500,000 and over $1 million for construction must submit a subcontracting plan. Public Law 99-661 and Public Law 100-180 affect Department of Defense purchasing as it relates to small and small disadvantaged business (SDB) procurement. (See Section 1: Legislation for additional information on these and other statutes which impact procurement.)

The regulations covering all federal contracts are contained in the Federal Acquisition Regulations (FAR). In some cases there are supplements to the FAR, as in the case of DFAR, which regulates contracts with the Department of Defense, and TAR, which relates to the Department of Transportation. A copy of the FAR may be purchased from the Superintendent of Documents, US Government Printing Office, Washington, DC 20402 - Phone (202) 512-1800.

NOTE: *Because the FAR is very complex and detailed, this brief summary is in no way intended to list out all the particulars of these regulations. It is recommended you obtain a current copy.*

FAR Definitions

The following definitions are generally used:

SDB — A business which meets the federal government's definition of small (as defined by the Small Business Administration) and which is at least 51% owned and controlled by a member of a minority group which the government has declared as socially or economically disadvantaged.

Prime Contractor — Company receiving a DOD contract of $100,000 or more.

Office of Small and Disadvantaged Business Utilization — (OSDBU) - Each Federal Agency with significant procurement authority has an Office of Small and Disadvantaged Business Utilization (OSDBU). Their charge is to promote S/SDB participation in procurement opportunities.

Small and Disadvantaged Business Utilization Specialists — (SADBUS) - Staff of OSDBU who work with S/SDBs and monitor compliance of subcontracting plans.

SBLO — Small Business Liaison Officer. Person designated by prime contractors as responsible for company's small and SDB business program.

General Guidelines

In contracting with Federal agencies, all solicitations for negotiated or formally advertised contracts greater than $500,000 or $1,000,000 for construction contracts shall include a provision which requires the prime contractor to submit a detailed subcontracting plan prior to the award. Negotiated contracts cannot be awarded until an acceptable plan has been negotiated, and subcontracting plans are incorporated as part of the contract awarded. (See Contract Bundling, Section 5: Department of Defense).

Failure to comply in good faith will be a material breach of the contract/subcontract. If a breach occurs in a prime contract, the contracting officer may:

- terminate the contract pursuant to the termination for default clause.
- reduce the contract price.
- negotiate a revised subcontracting plan to correct deficiencies.
- institute other measures.

Mandatory Components of a Subcontracting Plan Include:

- Separate percentage goals for use of small businesses/SDBs as subcontractors. (Example: 5% & 20% goal means 5% SDB goal wrapped into an overall 20% small business goal.)
- Name and responsibilities of the prime's subcontracting administrator (SBLO).
- Description of what the prime will do to ensure that small businesses and SDBs have opportunities to compete fairly.
- Assurance that the prime contractor will include the Utilization of Small and Disadvantaged Business Concerns clause in subcontracts; ensure that non-small business subcontractors adopt a similar small business/SDB utilization subcontracting plan. (Flow down clause. For more information review the FAR)
- Assurance that the prime will cooperate in any studies or surveys which may be required, submit periodic reports which allow the Government to determine the extent of compliance, submit Subcontracting Report for Individual Contracts (SF 294).
- Document efforts prime contractor has made to comply with the requirements and goals in the plan, including source lists and a description of efforts to locate SDBs.

Subcontracting plans are submitted to, approved and monitored by, the appropriate contracting officer. (For more information on the provisions of the subcontracting plan, please review the FAR.)

OFFICE OF SMALL AND DISADVANTAGED BUSINESS UTILIZATION (OSDBU)

The OSBDU's offer small business information on procurement opportunities, guidance on procurement procedures, and identification of both prime and subcontracting opportunities.

Major Federal Executive Procurement Agencies

Department of Agriculture
1400 Independence Ave SW
AG Stop 9501, Rm 1085
Washington, DC 20250-9501
(202) 720-7117
Fax (202) 720-3001
www.usda.gov/osdbu

Department of the Air Force
901 N Stuart Street, Ste 802
Arlington, VA 22203
(703) 696-1103
Fax (703) 696-1170
www.selltoairforce.org

Department of the Army
106 Army Pentagon, Rm 3B514
5810 Washington, DC 20310-0106
(703) 697-2868
Fax (703) 693-3898
www.sellingtoarmy.info

Department of Commerce
1401 Constitution Ave NW, Rm H6411
Washington, DC 20230
(202) 482-1472
Fax (202) 482-0501
www.osec.doc.gov/osdbu

Department of Defense
201 12th Street South, Ste 406
Arlington, VA 22202
(703) 604-0157 ext 151
Fax (703) 604-0025
www.acq.osd.mil/osbp/

Defense Logistics Agency
8725 John J Kingman Rd, DB room 1127
Ft Belvoir, VA 22060-6221
(703) 767-9465 or (800) 523-2601
www.dla.mil/db

Department of Education
400 Maryland Ave SW room 705 PCP
Washington, DC 20202-0521
(800) 872-5327
Fax (202) 245-6304
www.ed.gov/about/offices/list/ods/index.html

Department of Energy
1000 Independence Ave SW, Rm 148
Washington, DC 20585
(202) 586-7377
Fax (202) 586-5488
http://smallbusiness.doe.gov

Environmental Protection Agency
1200 Pennsylvania Ave NW
Mail Code 1230T
Washington, DC 20460
(202) 566-2075
www.epa.gov/osdbu

General Services Administration
Office of Small Business Utilization
1800 F St NW, Rm 6029
Washington, DC 20405
(202) 501-1021
Fax (202) 208-5938
www.gsa.gov/sbu

Department of Health and Human Services
Hubert H Humphrey Bldg
200 Independence Ave SW, Rm 360G
Washington, DC 20201
(202) 690-7235
Fax (202) 260-4872
www.hhs.gov/osdbu/

Department of Homeland Security
7th & D Streets, Rm 3514
Washington, DC 20528
(202) 692-4343
Fax (202) 777-8467
www.dhs.gov/openforbusiness

Department of Housing and Urban Development
451 Seventh Street,room 3130
Washington, DC 20410-1000
(202) 708-1428
Fax (202) 708-7642
www.hud.gov/smallbusiness

Department of the Interior
1849 C St NW, Rm 2252
Washington, DC 20240
(202) 208-3493
Fax (202) 208-7444
www.doi.gov/osdbu/

Department of Justice
1331 Pennsylvania Ave NW
National Place (The Shops), Rm 1010
Washington, DC 20530
(202) 616-0521
Fax (202) 616-1717
www.usdoj.gov/jmd/osdbu/

Department of Labor
200 Constitution Ave NW, Rm C2318
Washington, DC 20210
(202) 693-6460
Fax (202) 693-6485
www.dol.gov/dol/business.htm

National Aeronautics and Space Administration
300 E St SW rm 5C39
Washington, DC 20546
(202) 358-2088
Fax (202) 358-3261
www.osdbu.nasa.gov

Department of the Navy
720 Kennon St SE, Bldg 36 Rm 207
Washington, DC 20374-5015
(202) 685-6485
Fax (202) 685-6865
www.donhq.navy.mil/OSBP

Department of State
OSDBU (SA-6), Rm L500
Washington, DC 20522-0602
(703) 875-6822
Fax (703) 875-6825
www.state.gov/m/a/sdbu/

Social Security Administration
Office of Acquisition and Grants
7111 Security Blvd, 1st Fl
Baltimore, MD 21244
(410) 965-7467
Fax (410) 597-1548

Department of Transportation
400 7th St SW, Rm 9414
Washington, DC 20590
(202) 366-1930
Fax (202) 366-7538
http://osdbuweb.dot.gov/index.cfm

Department of the Treasury
1500 Pennsylvania Ave NW
655 15th St, Rm 6099
Washington, DC 20220
(202) 622-0530
Fax (202) 622-4963
www.treas.gov/sba

Department of Veterans Affairs
810 Vermont Ave NW
OSDBU 00VE, Rm 620
Washington, DC 20420
(202) 565-8124
Fax (202) 565-8156
www.va.gov/osdbu/

Other Procurement Agencies, Bureaus and Organizations

US Agency for International Development
OSDBU/MRC, Rm 7.8-E
Ronald Reagan Bldg
1300 Pennsylvania Ave NW
Washington, DC 20523
(202) 712-1500
Fax (202) 216-3056
www.usaid.gov/

Consumer Product Safety Commission
Small Business Ombudsman
4330 East West Hwy
Bethesda, MD 20814
(301) 504-7923
Fax (301) 504-0124

Corporation for National and Community Svc
Office of the Chief Financial Officer
1201 NY Ave NW
Washington, DC 20525
(202) 606-6988
Fax (202) 606-3488

Army Corp of Engineers
Pulaski Bldg, Rm 4117
441 G Street
Washington, DC 20314
(202) 761-0011
Fax (202) 761-1803

Defense Human Resources Activity
4040 N Fairfax Dr, Ste 200
Arlington, VA 22203-1613
(703) 696-1036

Defense Threat Reduction Agency
8725 John J Kingman Rd Stop 6201
Fort Belvoir, VA 22060
(703) 767-5870

Missile Defense Organization
7100 MDA/SB Defense Pentagon
Washington, DC 20301-7100
(703) 553-3404

Defense Intelligence Agency, Virginia Contracting Activity (VACA)
Office of Small & Disadvantaged Business Utilization
Bldg 6000, Bolling Air Force Base
Washington, DC 20340
(202) 231-2166
Fax (202) 231-2831

Defense Contract Management Agency (DCMA)
6350 Walker Ln
Alexandria, VA 22310
(703) 428-0786
Fax (703) 428-3578

Defense Information Systems Agency (DISA)
701 S Courthouse Rd, D04 Rm 1108B
Arlington, VA 22204-2199
(703) 607-6436
Fax (703) 607-4173
www.disa.mil/main/sadbu.html

Export-Import Bank of the US
811 Vermont Ave NW rm 1023
Washington, DC 20571
(202) 565-3338
Fax (202) 565-3528

Farm Credit Administration
1501 Farm Credit Dr
McLean, VA 22102-5090
(703) 883-4056

Federal Communications Commission
Office of Communications Business Opportunities
445 12th St SW
Washington, DC 20554
(202) 418-0990
Fax (202) 418-0235

Federal Maritime Commission
800 North Capitol St, Rm 926
Washington, DC 20573
(202) 523-5900
Fax (202) 523-3782

Federal Mediation & Conciliation Service (FMCS)
2100 K St, NW, 1st Fl
Washington, DC 20427
(202) 606-8100

Federal Trade Commission
Acquisitions Branch, Rm 701
600 & Pennsylvania Ave NW
Washington, DC 20580
(202) 326-2258
www.ftc.gov/procurement

Office of Civil Rights
200 Independence Ave SW, Room 509f
Washington, DC 20201
(800) 368-1019
Fax (202) 366-7717

Government Accountability Office (GAO)
441 G St NW, Rm 6B46
Washington, DC 20548
(202) 512-3000
Fax (202) 512-2879

US Government Printing Office
General Procurement Division
Rm A332, Stop MMG
732 North Capitol St NW
Washington, DC 20401
(202) 512-0916
Fax (202) 512-0975

United States International Trade Commission
500E St SW, Rm 214
Washington, DC 20436
(202) 205-2730
Fax (202) 205-2150

Library of Congress
Office of Contracts
101 Independence Ave SE
Washington, DC 20540-9411
(202) 707-9129
Fax (202) 707-8611

National Archives and Records Administration
Government Contracting Division
8601 Adelphi Rd, Rm 3360
College Park, MD 20740-6001
(301) 837-1489
Fax (301)837-3227

National Endowment for Humanities
1100 Pennsylvania Ave NW, Rm 201
Washington, DC 20506
(202) 606-8233
Fax (202) 606-8243

National Labor Relations Board
1099 14th St, NW, Ste 7108
Washington, DC 20570
(202) 273-3890
Fax (202) 273-2928

National Science Foundation
4201 Wilson Blvd, Rm 527
Arlington, VA 22230
(703) 292-7082
Fax (703) 292-9055
www.nsf.gov/

Nuclear Regulatory Commission
11545 Rockville Pike MS-T2F18
Washington, DC 20852
(301) 415-7380/7381
Fax (301) 415-5953

Office of Personnel Management
1900 E St NW, Rm 3B-427
Washington, DC 20415
(202) 606-2180
Fax (202) 606-1464

Department of Justice - Federal Bureau of Prisons
1331 Pennsylvania Ave, Rm 1010
Washington, DC 20530
(202) 616-0521
Fax (202) 616-1717

Indian Health Service
Loan Repayment Program
Twinbrook Metro Plaza, Ste 100A
12300 Twinbrook Parkway
Rockville, MD 20852
(301) 443-1480
Fax (301) 443-1329

Overseas Private Investment Corporation
1100 New York Ave NW
Washington, DC 20527
(202) 336-8499
Fax (202) 408-9859

Peace Corps
1100 20th St NW
Washington, DC 20526
(202) 692-1630
Fax (202) 692-1621

US Postal Service
475 L'Enfant Plaza West SW, Rm 4430
Washington, DC 20260-5616
(202) 268-4633
Fax (202) 268-4012
www.usps.gov/purchasing

US Rail Road Retirement Board
1310 G St NW, Ste 500
Washington, DC 20005
(202) 272-7742
Fax (202) 272-7728
www.rrb.gov

Federal Deposit Insurance Corporation
3501 Fairfax Drive rm E2014
Arlington, VA 22226
(703) 562-6070
Fax (703) 562-6069

Federal Election Commission
5th St NW, Rm 7201
Washington, DC 20549
(202) 942-8945
Fax (202) 942-9365

US Small Business Administration
409 3rd St SW, 8th Fl
Washington, DC 20416
(202) 205-6385

Smithsonian Institute
600 Maryland Ave SW suite 2091 MRD 521
Washington, DC 20024
(202) 633-6430
Fax (202) 633-6427
www.si.edu/oeema/sdbu.htm

Transit Authority (Metro)
600 Fifth Street, NW
Washington, DC 20001
(202) 962-2464
Fax (202) 962-2471

Liaison Offices

Committee for Purchase from People who are Blind or Severely Disabled
1421 Jefferson Davis Hwy
Jefferson Plaza 2, Ste 10800
Arlington, VA 22243-0001
(703) 603-7740
Fax (703) 603-0655

Committee on Small Business and Entrepreneurship
Russell Office Bldg, Rm 428A
Washington, DC 20510
(202)224-5175 or (202) 224-8496
Fax (202) 224-4885 or (202) 224-5619

House Committee on Small Business
Rayburn Bldg, Rm 2361
Washington, DC 20515-6315
(202) 225-5821 or (202) 225-2361

International Franchise Association
1350 New York Ave NW, Ste 900
Washington, DC 20037
(202) 662-0784
Fax (202) 628-0812

US Department of Commerce
Minority Business Development Agency
14th & Constitution Ave NW, Rm H5055
Washington, DC 20230
(202) 482-2332
Fax (202) 501-4698

National Counsel
15 West 39th St, 9th Flr
New York, NY 10018
(212) 944-2430
Fax (212) 719-9611

George Mason University
Procurement Technical Assistance Program
4031 University Dr, Ste 200
Fairfax, VA 22030
(703) 277-7700
Fax (703) 352-8195

Office of Federal Procurement Policy
725 17th St NW, Rm 9013
Washington, DC 20503
(202) 395-6811

Committee on Small Business & Entrepreneurship
Russell Office Bldg, Rm 428A
Washington, DC 20510
(202)224-5175 or (202) 224-8496
Fax (202) 224-4885 or (202) 224-5619
www.sbc.senate.gov

SECTION 10

HISTORICALLY UNDERUTILIZED BUSINESS ZONES (HUBZones)

https://eweb1.sba.gov/hubzone/internet/

The HUBZone Empowerment Contracting program provides federal contracting opportunities for qualified small businesses located in distressed areas. Fostering the growth of these federal contractors as viable businesses, for the long term, helps to empower communities, create jobs, and attract private investment.

Program History

The HUBZone Empowerment Contracting program was enacted into law as part of the Small Business Reauthorization Act of 1997. The program falls under the auspices of the US Small Business Administration. The program encourages economic development in historically underutilized business zones - "HUBZones" - through the establishment of preferences.

SBA's HUBZone program is in line with the efforts of both the Administration and Congress to promote economic development and employment growth in distressed areas by providing access to more Federal contracting opportunities.

How the HUBZone Program Works

The US Small Business Administration (SBA) regulates and implements the program, determines which businesses are eligible to receive HUBZone contracts, maintains a listing of qualified HUBZone small businesses Federal agencies can use to locate vendors, adjudicates protests of eligibility to receive HUBZone contracts, and reports to the Congress on the program's impact on employment and investment in HUBZone areas.

Publication of Final Rule

The final rule for the HUBZone Empowerment Contracting Program was published on June 11, 1998. The interim Federal Acquisition Regulation (FAR) FAC 97-10, FAR Case 97-307 was published on December 18, 1998 to give effect to the contracting component of the program on January 4, 1999. The comment period for the FAR expired on February 18, 1999.

Eligibility

A small business meets all of the following criteria to qualify for the HUBZone program:

- it must be located in a "historically underutilized business zone,"
- it must be owned and controlled by one or more U.S. Citizens, and
- at least 35% of its employees must reside in a HUB Zone.

Historically Underutilized Business Zone

A "HUBZone" is an area that is located in one or more of the following:

- a qualified census tract (as defined in section 42(d)(5)(C)(i)(I) of the Internal Revenue Code of 1986);
- a qualified "non-metropolitan county" (as defined in section 143(k)(2)(B) of the Internal Revenue Code of 1986) with a median household income of less than 80 percent of the State median household income or with an unemployment rate of not less than 140 percent of the statewide average, based on U.S. Department of Labor recent data; or
- lands within the boundaries of federally recognized Indian reservations.

Types of HUBZone Contracts

A **competitive** HUBZone contract can be awarded if the contracting officer has a reasonable expectation that at least two qualified HUBZone small businesses will submit offers and that the contract can be awarded at a fair market price.

A **sole source** HUBZone contract can be awarded if the contracting officer does not have a reasonable expectation that two or more qualified HUBZone small businesses will submit offers, determines that the qualified

HUBZone small business is responsible, and determines that the contract can be awarded at a fair price. The government estimate cannot exceed $5 million for manufacturing requirements or $3 million for all other requirements.

A **full and open competition** contract can be awarded with a price evaluation preference. The offer of the HUBZone small business will be considered lower than the offer of a non-HUBZone/non-small business-providing that the offer of the HUBZone small business is not more than 10 percent higher.

Goaling

The Small Business Reauthorization Act of 1997 increases the overall government wide procurement goal for small business from 20% to 23%. The statute sets the goal for HUBZone contracts as follows: 1999 - 1%; 2000 - 1 ½ %; 2001 - 2%; 2002 - 2 ½ %; 2003; and each year thereafter - 3%.

Affected Federal Agencies

As of Octover 1, 2000, all Federal agencies are subject to the requirements of the HUBZone Program.

SECTION 11

WOMEN'S BUSINESS RESOURCES

Small Business Administration
Office of Women's Business Ownership (OWBO)
409 Third Street SW, 6th Floor
Washington, DC 20416
(202) 205-6673
www.sba.gov/womeninbusiness
owbo@sba.gov

The Office of Women's Business ownership
America's 10.6 million women-owned businesses employ 19.1 million people and contribute $2.46 trillion to the economy. Yet women continue to face unique obstacles in the world of business. The US Small Business Administration is doing more than ever to help level the playing field for women entrepreneurs, and the SBA's Office of Women's Business Ownership (OWBO) is leading the way.

OWBO promotes the growth of women-owned businesses through programs that address business training and technical assistance, and provide access to credit and capital, federal contracts, and international trade opportunities. With a women's business ownership representative in every SBA district office, a nationwide network of mentoring roundtables, women's business centers in nearly every state and territory, women-owned venture capital companies, and the Online Women's Business Center, OWBO is helping unprecedented numbers of women start and build successful businesses. At every stage of developing and expanding a successful business, the Office of Women's Business Ownership is here to counsel, teach, encourage and inspire.

Mission
To assist women achieve their dreams and improve their communities by helping them start and run successful businesses, regardless of social or financial disadvantage, race, ethnicity or business background.

The Office of Women's Business Ownership and the Online Women's Business Center are integral components of Entrepreneurial Development's network of training and counseling services.

SBA WOMEN'S BUSINESS OWNERSHIP REPRESENTATIVES

The Office of Women's Business Ownership is an integral component of Entrepreneurial Development's network of training and counseling services.

ALASKA
510 L St, Ste 310
Anchorage, AK 99501
(907) 271-4022

ALABAMA
801 Tom Martin Drive suite 201
Birmingham, AL 35211
(205) 290-7101
Fax (205) 290-7404

ARKANSAS
2120 Riverfront Dr, Ste 250
Little Rock, AR 72202
(501) 324-7379 x 297
Fax (501) 324-7394

ARIZONA
2828 N Central Ave, Ste 800
Phoenix, AZ 85004-1093
(602) 745-7200
Fax (202) 745-7210

CALIFORNIA
2719 N Air Fresno Dr, Ste 200
Fresno, CA 93727
(559) 487-5791 x 137
Fax (559) 487-5636

550 West C St, Ste 550
San Diego, CA 92101-3500
(619) 557-5894
Fax (619) 557-6998

455 Market Street 6th floor
San Francisco, CA 94105
(415) 744-6820

200 W Santa Ana Blvd, Ste 700
Santa Ana, CA 92701-4134
(714) 550-7420
Fax (714) 550-0191

COLORADO
721 19th St, Rm 426
Denver, CO 80202
(303) 844-2607 x 226

CONNECTICUT
330 Main St, 2nd Fl
Hartford, CT 06106
(860) 240-4700
Fax (202) 481-1582

DELAWARE
Nemours Building
1007 N Orange St., Ste 1120
Wilmington DE 19801
(302) 573-6294 ext.225

DISTRICT OF COLUMBIA
American Bar Association Bldg
740 15th St NW, sTE 300
Washington, DC 20005
(202) 272-0345
Fax (202) 481-2768

FLORIDA
7825 Baymeadows Way, Ste 100B
Jacksonville, FL 32256-7504
(904) 443-1900

100 S Biscayne Blvd, 7th Fl
Miami, FL 33131
(305) 536-5521 x 152
Fax (305) 536-5058

GEORGIA
233 Peachtree St NE, Ste 1900
Atlanta, GA 30303
(404) 331-0100 x 405

GUAM
400 Route 8, Ste 302, First Hawaiian Bank Building
Mongmong, GM 96927
(671) 472-7419
Fax (671) 472-7365

HAWAII
300 Ala Moana Blvd , Rm 2-235
Honolulu, HI 96850
(808) 541-2990 ext 215 or 205
Fax (808) 541-2976

IDAHO
380 E Parkcenter Blvd, Ste 330
Boise, ID 83706
(208) 334-1696
Fax (208) 334-9353

ILLINOIS
3330 Ginger Crk Rd, Ste B East
Springfield, IL 62711
(217) 793-5020 x 107
Fax (217) 793-5025

500 W Madison Street suite 1250
Chicago, IL 60661
(312) 353-4528
Fax (312)886-5688

INDIANA
8500 Keystone Crossing suite 400
Indianapolis, IN 46240
(317) 226-7272

IOWA
2750 1st Ave NE, Ste 350
Cedar Rapids, IA 52402-4831
(319) 362-6405 x 207
Fax (202) 481-0649

210 Walnut St
Des Moines, IA 50309-2186
(515) 284-4422

KANSAS
271 W 3rd St North, Ste 2500
Wichita, KS 67202-1212
(316) 269-6616

KENTUCKY
600 Dr MLK, Jr Pl, Rm 188
Louisville, KY 40202
(502) 582-5971 x 233

LOUISIANA
365 Canal St, Ste 2820
New Orleans, LA 70130
(504) 589-6685

MAINE
68 Sewall St
Augusta, ME 04330
(207) 622-8274
Fax (202) 481-4827

MARYLAND
10 S Howard St
Baltimore, MD 21201
(410) 962-6195 x 337
Fax (202) 481-5612

MASSACHUSETTS
10 Causeway St, Rm 265
Boston, MA 02222
(617) 565-5590

MICHIGAN
477 Michigan Ave, Ste 515
Detroit, MI 48226
(313) 226-6075 x 223
Fax (202) 481-0675

MINNESOTA
100 N Sixth St, Ste 610c
Minneapolis, MN 55403
(612) 370-2324
Fax (202) 481-0139

MISSISSIPPI
Am South Plaza, Ste 900
210 E Capitol
Jackson, MS 39201
(601) 965-5629
Fax (601) 965-4294

MISSOURI
830 E Primrose, #101
Springfield, MO 65807-5254
(417) 890-8501 x 203
Fax (202) 481-2422

Commerce Bank Building
1000 Walnut St
Kansas City MO 64106
(816) 426-4900
Fax (202) 481-0362

200 N Broadway, Ste 1500
St Louis, MO 63102
(314) 539-6600 x 223
Fax (314) 539-3785

MONTANA
10 West 15th St, Ste 1100
Helena, MT 59626
(406) 441-1081
Fax (202) 481-1090

NEBRASKA
10675 Bedford Avenue Ste 100
Omaha, NE 68134
(402) 221-4691
Fax (202) 481-2420 or 0393

NEW HAMPSHIRE
55 Pleasant Street, Ste 3101
Concord, NH 03301
(603) 225-1400
Fax (202) 481-0159

NEW JERSEY
Two Gateway Center, 15th Fl
Hamilton, NJ 07102
(973) 645-2434
Fax (202) 481-2837

NEW MEXICO
625 Silver SW, Rm 320
Albuquerque, NM 87102
(505) 248-8225
Fax (202) 248-8246

NEW YORK
130 S Elmwood St
Buffalo, NY 14202
(716)551-4301 ext 303
Fax(716) 551-4418

26 Federal Plaza, Rm 3100
New York, NY 10278
(212) 264-4354
Fax (212) 264-4963

401 S Salina St, 5th Fl
Syracuse, NY 13202
(315) 471-9393 x 241
Fax (315) 471-9393

NEVADA
400 South Fourth St, Ste 250
Las Vegas, NV 89101
(702) 388-6674/(775) 827-4865
Fax (702)388-6469/(775)481-0999

NORTH CAROLINA
6302 Fairview Road, Ste 300
Charlotte, NC 28210
(704) 344-6811
Fax (704) 344-6769

NORTH DAKOTA
657 2nd Ave N Rm 218
Bismarck, ND 58108-3086
(701) 239-5131
Fax (202) 239-5645

OHIO
1350 Euclid Ave Ste 211
Cleveland, OH 44115
(216) 522-4180
Fax (216) 522-2038

401 N Front Street Ste 200
Columbus, OH 43215-2542
(614) 469-6860
Fax (202) 481-5520

OKLAHOMA
310 NW 6th Street Ste 116
Oklahoma City, OK 73102
(405) 609-8000
Fax (202) 481-5837

OREGON
ODS Building
601 SW 2nd Ave, Ste 950
Portland, OR 97204-3154
(503) 326-2682
Fax (503) 326-2808

PENNSYLVANIA
Parkview Tower
1150 First Avenue, Ste 10001
King of Prussia, PA 19406
(610) 382-3062
Fax (202) 481-0193

411 7th Avenue Ste1450
Pittsburgh, PA 15219
(412) 395-6560
Fax (412) 395-6562

PUERTO RICO
252 Ponce De Leon Blvd
Citibank Tower Ste 200
San Juan, PR 00918
(787) 766-5572
Fax (787) 766-5309

RHODE ISLAND
380 Westminster Mall, Rm 511
Providence, RI 02903
(401) 528-4561
Fax (202) 481-4353

SOUTH CAROLINA
1835 Assembly St, Rm 1425
Columbia, SC 29201
(803) 765-5377
Fax (803) 765-5962

SOUTH DAKOTA
2329 North Career Ave, Ste 105
Sioux Falls, SD 57107
(605) 330-4243
Fax (605) 330-4215

TENNESSEE
50 Vantage Way, Ste 201
Nashville, TN 37228
(615) 736-5881 x 241
Fax (615) 736-7232

TEXAS
3649 Leopard St, Ste 411
Corpus Christi, TX 78476
(361) 879-0017
Fax (361) 879-0764

211 N Florence St., 2nd Fl,Ste 201
El Paso, TX 79901
(915) 834-4600
Fax (915) 834-4689

4300 Amon Carter Blvd, #114
Fort Worth, TX 76155
(817) 684-5500
Fax (817) 684-5516

222 E Van Buren St, Ste 500
Harlingen, TX 78550
(956) 427-8533
Fax (956) 427-8537

8701 South Gessner Dr, Ste 1200
Houston, TX 77074
(713) 773-6500 x 226
Fax (713) 773-6550

1205 Texas Ave, Ste 408
Lubbock, TX 79401
(806) 472-7462
Fax (806) 472-7487

17319 San Pedro, Bldg 2, Ste 200
San Antonio, TX 78232
(210) 403-5900
Fax (210) 403-5936

VIRGIN ISLANDS
Sunny Isle Professional Bldg
Stes 5 & 6
Christensted USVI 00820
(340) 778-5380 ext 22
Fax (202) 481-0581

UTAH
125 S State St Rm 2227
Salt Lake City, UT 84138
(801) 524-3209

VIRGINIA
400 N 8th St, Ste 1150
Richmond, VA 23219-4829
(804) 771-2400
Fax (804) 771-2764

VERMONT
87 State St, Rm 205
Montpelier, VT 05601
(802) 828-4422 x 206
Fax (202) 481-0525

WASHINGTON
2401 Fourth Ave Ste 450
Fouth & Battery Bldg
Seattle, WA 98121
(206) 553-7310
Fax (202) 481-5587 or 4121

WISCONSIN
310 W Wisconsin Ave, #400
Milwaukee, WI 53203
(414) 297-3941
Fax (414) 297-1377

WEST VIRGINIA
405 Capitol Street Ste 412
Charleston WV 25301
(304)347-5220
Fax (202) 481-1864

WYOMING
100 East B St, Rm 4001
Casper, WY 82602
(307) 261-6500
Fax (307) 261-6535

SMALL BUSINESS ADMINISTRATION'S WOMEN'S BUSINESS CENTERS

www.sba.gov/womeninbusiness/wbcs.html

Each women's business center provides assistance and/or training in finance, management, marketing, procurement and the Internet, as well addressing specialized topics such as home-based businesses, corporate executive downsizing and welfare-to-work. All provide individual business counseling and access to the SBA's programs and services; a number are also intermediaries for the SBA's MicroLoan and Loan Prequalification programs. Each WBC tailors its programs to the needs of its constituency; many offer programs and counseling in two or more languages. The following is contact information and a brief description of each WBC.

ALABAMA

Elizabeth Conwell Schlarb Foundation for Women Entrepreneurs
2 North 20th St, Ste 830
Birmingham, AL 35203
(205) 453-0249
Fax (205) 453-0253
www.cawbc.org

Women's Business Center of North Alabama
225 Church Street
Huntsville, AL 35801
(256) 535-2038
Fax (256) 535-2015
www.wbcna.org

Women's Business Center of Southern Alabama
1301 Azalea Rd, Ste 201A
Mobile, AL 36693
(251) 660-2725
Fax (251) 660-8854
www.womenbiz.biz

ALASKA

YWCA Anchorage
WOMEN$ Finances Program
324 E 5th Ave
Anchorage, AK 99501
(907) 644-9600
Fax (907) 644-9650
www.ywcaak.org

AMERICAN SAMOA

Native American Samoan Advisory Council
PO Box 6849
Pago Pago, AS 96799
011/(684) 699-8739
Fax 011/(684) 699-6580
http://web.mac.com/wbcas/site/ASWBC_Homepage.html

ARIZONA

Microbusiness Advancement Center of Southern Alabama
330 N Commerce Park Loop Ste 160
Tucson, AZ 85745
(520) 620-1241 x107
Fax (520) 622-2235
www.mac-sa.org

ARKANSAS

Southern Good Faith Fund
2304 W 29th Ave
Pine Bluff, AR 71603
(870) 535-6233 x38
Fax (870) 535-0741
www.southerngff.org

CALIFORNIA

Founsation for California State University/ San Bernandino Inland Empire WBC
200 E. Airport Drive, Ste 155
San Bernandino, CA 92408
(909) 890-1242
Fax (909)537-7609
www.csusb.org

Anew America Community Corporation
1918 University Ave, Ste 3A
Berkeley, CA 94704
(510) 540-7785 x302
Fax (510) 540-7786
www.anewamerica.org

Asian Pacific Islander SB Program- WBC
231 E Third St, G106
Los Angeles, CA 90013
(213) 473 1605
Fax (213) 473-1601
www.itsc.org

CHARO Community Development Corporation
4301 East Valley Blvd
Los Angeles, CA 90032
(323) 269-1206
Fax (323) 343-9484
www.charocorp.org

Mission Community Services Corp
4111 Broad Street Ste A4
San Luis Obispo, CA 93401
(805) 595-1356
Fax (805) 595-1358
www.mcscorp.org

Pacific Asian Consortium in Employment (PACE)
1055 Wilshire Blvd, Ste 1475
Los Angeles, CA 90017
(213) 989-3153
Fax (213) 353-4665
www.pacela.org

Rancho Santiago Comm. College Institute for Women Entrepreneurs
2323 N Broadway
Santa Ana, CA 92706
(714) 480-7455
Fax (714) 647-1168
www.rsccd.org

Renaissance Entrepreneurship Center
275 Fifth St
San Francisco, CA 94103-4120
(415) 348-6237
Fax (415) 541-8589
www.rencenter.org

Valley Economic Development Center
5121 Van Nuys Blvd, Ste 300
Van Nuys, CA 91403
(818) 907-9922
www.vedc.org

Women's Initiative for Self Employment (WISE)
519 17th Street, Ste 110
Oakland, CA 94612
(510) 287-3100
www.womensinitiative.org

Women's Economic Venture of Santa Barbara
333 S Salinas St
Santa Barbara, CA 93101
(805) 965-6073 x104
Fax (805) 962-1396
www.wevonline.org

COLORADO

Mi Casa Resource Center for Women, Inc
360 Acoma Street
Denver, CO 80223
(303) 573-1302
Fax (719) 542-1006
www.micasadenver.org

CONNECTICUT

University of Hartford
50 Elizabeth St
Hartford, CT 06105
(860) 768-5681
Fax (860) 768-5622
www.entrepreneurialctr.org

Women's Business Development Center (WBDC)
Government Center
888 Washington Blvd. 10th floor
Stamford, CT 06901
(203) 353-1750
Fax (203) 353-1084
www.ctwbdc.org

DELEWARE

YWCA Deleware
Center for Women's Entrepreneurship
153 E. Chesnut Hill Road, Ste 102
Newark, DE 18713
(302) 224-4060
www.ywcade.org

DISTRICT OF COLUMBIA

Women's Business Center, Inc
1001 Connecticut Ave NW, Ste 312
Washington, DC 20036
(202) 785-4922
Fax (202) 785-4110
www.womensbusinesscenter.org

FLORIDA

Florida Institute of Technology
150 W University Blvd.
Melbourne, FL 32901
(321) 674-7006
www.fit.edu

Center for Technology Enterprise.
401 W Atlantic Avenue Ste 9
Delray Beach, FL 33444
(561) 265-3790 ext 111
Fax (561) 265-0806
www.flwbc.org

Jacksonville WBC
3 Independent Drive
Jacksonville, FL 32202
(904) 924-1100 x252
Fax (904) 366-6640
www.myjaxchamber.com

GEORGIA

The Edge Connection
1000 Chastain Rd, #3305
Kennesaw, GA 30144
(770) 499-3228
Fax (770) 499-3636
www.kennesaw.org

Women's Economic Development Agency (WEDA)
675 Metropolitan Pkwy SW
Atlanta, GA 30310
(678) 904-2201
Fax (678) 904-2205
www.weda-atlanta.org

HAWAII

Hawaii Women's Business Center
1041 Nuuanu Ave, Ste A
Honolulu, HI 96817
(808) 526-1001
Fax (808) 550-0724
www.hwbc.org

ILLINOIS

Women's Business Development Center
8 South Michigan Ave, Ste 400
Chicago, IL 60603
(312) 853-3477 x38
Fax (312) 853-0145
www.wbdc.org

INDIANA
Business Ownership Initiatives of the Central Indiana WBC
4755 Kingsway Drive, Ste 314
Indianapolis, IN 46205
(317) 917-3266 ext 101
Fax (317) 916-8921
www.businessownership.org

Women's Enterprise, A Program of the Fort Wayne's Women's Bureau
3521 Lake Ave, Ste 1
Fort Wayne, IN 46805-5533
(260) 424-7977
Fax (260) 426-7576
www.womensenterprise.org

IOWA
ISED Ventures/ Iowa Womens Enterprise Center
1111 Ninth Street Ste 380
Des Moines, IA 50314
(515) 283-0940 ext 30
Fax (515) 283-0348
www.ised.org

KANSAS
Enterprise Center of Johnson Co.
8527 Bluejacket St
Lenexa, KS 66214
(913) 492-5922
Fax (913) 888-6928
www.kansaswbc.com

LOUISIANA
ULGNO
365 Canal St, Ste 2820
New Orleans, LA 70119
(504) 620-9645
Fax (504) 620-9659
www.urbanleagueneworleans.org/

Enterprise Consortium of the Gulf Coast
110 Travis Street, Ste 92
Lafayette, LA 70503
(337) 889-0211
www.ecgcwbc.com

MAINE
Coastal Enterprises Inc (CEI)
Rim Counties WBC
36 Water Street
Wiscasset, ME 04578
(207) 882-7552
Fax (207) 882-7308
www.ceimaine.org

MARYLAND
Women Entrepreneurs of Baltimore, Inc (WEB)
1118 Light St, Ste 101
Baltimore, MD 21230
(410) 727-4921 x20
Fax (410) 727-4989
www.webinc.org

MASSACHUSETTS
Eastern Massachusetts
Center for Women & Enterprise, Inc (CWE)
24 School Street, Ste 700
Boston MA 02109
(617) 536-0700
Fax (617) 536-7373
www.cweonline.org

Center for Women & Enterprise, Inc (CWE)
50 Elm St, Second Fl
Worcester MA 01609
(508) 363-2300
Fax (508) 363-2323
www.cweonline.org

MICHIGAN
Cornerstone Alliance
38 West Wall Street
Benton Harbor, MI 49022
(269) 925-6100
www.cstonealliance.org

Center of Economic Development
2002 Hogback Rd., Ste 12
Ann Harbor, MI 48105
(734) 677-1400
www.miceed.org

Grand Rapids Opportunities for Women
25 Sheldon St SE, Ste 210
Grand Rapids, MI 49503
(616) 458-3404
Fax (616) 458-6557
www.growbusiness.org

MINNESOTA
Northeast Entrepreneur Fund
8355 Unity Dr, Ste 100
Virginia, MN 55792
(800) 422-0374 ext 414
Fax (218) 749-5213
www.entreprenuerfund.org

WomenVenture
2324 University Ave West, Ste 120
St Paul, MN 55114
(651) 646-3808
Fax (651) 641-7223
www.womenventure.org

MISSISSIPPI
Crudup Ward Activity Center
656 Longview Street
Forest, MS 39074
(601) 469-3357
Fax (601) 469-3357
www.cwacine.org

MACE Women's Business Center
119 South Theobald St
Greenville, MS 38701
(662) 335-3523
Fax (662) 334-2939
www.deltamace.org

MISSOURI
Grace Hill WBC
2324 N Flourissant
St Louis, MO 63106
(314) 584-6840
Fax (314) 584-6850
www.gracehill.org

NEBRASKA
Rural Enterprise Assistance Project (REAP)
145 Main St
Lyons, NE 68038
(402) 643-2673
www.cfra.org/reap

NEVADA
Nevada Micro-Enterprise Development Corporation
1600 E Desert Inn Rd, Ste 203
Las Vegas, NV 89109
(702) 734-3555
Fax (702) 734-3530
www.4microbiz.org

NEW HAMPSHIRE
Women's Business Center, Inc
1555 Lafayette Rd, 2nd Fl
Portsmouth, NH 03801
(603) 430-2892 ext 4
Fax (603) 430-3706
www.womenbiz.org

NEW JERSEY
NJ Association of Women Business Owners-Peapack-Gladstone Bank
311 Main Street 2nd floor
Chatham, NJ 07928
(973) 507-9700
Fax (609) 581-6749
www.njawbo/wbc.org

Women's Venture Fund
76 Clinton Avenue
Newark, NJ 07114
(877) 444-0934
Fax (212) 868-9116
www.wvf-nj.org

NEW MEXICO
Women's Economic Self-Sufficiency Team (WESST) Corp
700 4th Street SW
Albuquerque, NM 87102
(505) 241-4767
Fax (505) 241-4766
www.wesst.org

Women's Economic Self-Sufficiency Team (WESST)
107 S First St
Gallup, NM 87301
(505) 863-3192
www.wesst.org

Women's Economic Self-Sufficiency Team (WESST) Corp
3900 Paseo de Sol, Ste 322A, Bldg I
Sante Fe, NM 87505
(505) 988-5030
Fax (505) 474-6687
www.wesst.org

Women's Economic Self-Sufficiency Team (WESST) Corp
200 West First St, Ste 527
Roswell, NM 88203
(505) 624-9850
Fax (505) 624-9845
www.wesst.org

NEW YORK
Canisius College - WBC
2365 Main St
Buffalo, NY 14214
(716) 888-8280
Fax (716) 888-6654
www.canisius.edu/

Business Outreach Center Network (BOC)
85 S Oxford St 2nd floor
Brooklyn, NY 11217
(718) 624-9115
(718) 246-1881
www.bocnet.org

ComLinks
343 West Main St
Malone, NY 12953
(518) 483-1261 ext 1019
Fax (518) 483-8599
www.comlinkscaa.org

Queens Economic Development Corp.
120-55 Queens Blvd, Ste 309
Queens, NY 11424
(718) 263-0546
Fax (718) 263-0594
www.queensny.org

Syracuse Women's Business Innovation Center/Syracuse Univ.
2610 South Salina Street
Syracuse NY 13205
(315) 443-0286
Fax (315)443-2654
www.wisecenter.org

The Local Development Corporation of East New York
80 Jamaica Ave 3rd floor
Brooklyn, NY 11207
(718) 385-6700 ext 24
Fax (718) 385-7505
www.ldceny.org

Hunts Point Economic Development Corporation
866 Hunts Point Ave
Bronx, NY 10474
(718) 842-8888
Fax (718) 620-1153
www.hpwbrc.org

WBC of New York State
200 Genesee St
Utica, NY 13502
(315) 733-9848
Fax (315) 733-0247
www.nywbc.org

Women's Enterprise Development Center, Inc
707 Weschester Ave Ste 213
White Plains, NY 10604
(914) 948-6098 ext 11
Fax (914) 948-6913
www.westchester.org

NORTH CAROLINA
Mountain Bizworks,
153 South Lexington Avenue
Ashville, NC 28801
(828) 253-2834 ext 28
Fax (828) 255-7953
www.mountainbizworks.org

North Carolina Institute of Minority Economic Development
114 West Parrish St, 4th Fl, PO Box 1331
Durham, NC 27701
(919) 956-8889
Fax (919) 688-4358
www.ncimed.com

The Women's Center of Fayetteville
230 Hay St
Fayetteville, NC 28301
(910) 323-3377
Fax (910) 323-8828
www.wcof.org

NORTH DAKOTA

The Center for Technology in Business
115 N 2nd Street
Bismarck, ND 58502
(701) 223-0707
Fax (701) 223-2507
www.trainingnd.com

OHIO

Alex Community Development Corporation
12200 Fairhill Rd
Cleveland, OH 44120
(216) 707-0777
www.alexcdc.com

OKLAHOMA

Rural Enterprises of Oklahoma, Inc (REO)
2912 Enterprise Blvd
Durant, OK 74701
(580) 924-5094
Fax (580) 920-2745
www.ruralenterprises.com

OREGON

ONABEN - A Native American Business Network
11825 SW Greenburg Rd, Ste B3
Tigard, OR 97223
(503) 998-9560
Fax (503) 968-1548
www.onaben.org

PENNSYLVANIA

Community First Fund
30 West Orange Street
Lancaster, PA 17603
(717) 393-2351
Fax (717) 290-7936
www.comfirstfund.org

Empowerment Group
2111 N Front Street
Philadelphia, PA 19122
(215) 427-9245
Fax (215) 427-0506
www.empowermentgroup.org

Seton Hill University/ E-Magnify
Seton Hill Drive
Greensburg, PA 15601
(724) 830-4612
Fax (724) 834-7131
www.esetonhill.com

Women's Business Development Center
1315 Walnut Street, Ste 1116
Philadelphia, PA 19107
(215) 790-5059
www.womensbdc.org

PUERTO RICO

Women's Business Institute (WBI)
PO Box 12383
San Juan, PR 00914-0383
(787) 726-7045 ext 25
Fax (787) 726-6550
www.mujeryempresas.org

RHODE ISLAND

Center for Women & Enterprise, Inc (CWE)
132 George M Cohan Blvd 2nd fl
Providence RI 02903
(401) 277-0800 ext 102
Fax (401) 277-1122
www.cweonline.org

SOUTH CAROLINA

SCWBC
1225 Laurel Street, Ste 405
Columbia, SC 29201
(803) 461-8900 ext 225
Fax (803) 799-7282
www.scwbc.org

TENNESSEE

Southeast Local Developmental Corporation
1000 Riverfront Parkway
PO Box 4757
Chattanooga, TN 37402
(423) 424-4220
Fax (423) 267-7705
www.sewbc.com

TEXAS

Business Invest In Growth, Inc. (BiGAUSTIN)
1050 E 11th St, Ste 350
Austin, TX 78702
(512) 928-8010
Fax (512) 926-2997
www.bigaustin.org

SW Community Investment Corp.
2836 West Trenton Road
Edinburg, TX 78539
(956) 618-2828
Fax (956) 618-2834
www.scictx.org

The South Texas Women's Business Center
100 W Houston Street, Ste 1900
San Antonio, TX 78283
(210) 207-0117
Fax (210) 207-3937
www.stwbc.com

Women's Business Border Center
2401 E Missouri
El Paso, TX 79901
(915) 566-4066
Fax (915) 566-9714
www.ephcc.org

UTAH

Salt Lake Chamber of Commerce
400 South Main St, Ste 600
Salt Lake City, UT 84111
(801) 328-5066
Fax (801) 328-5098
www.saltlakechamber.org

VERMONT

CVCAC -- WBC
88 S Main St
Barre, VT 05602
(802) 479-9813
Fax (802) 229-2141
www.vwbc.org

VIRGINIA

New Visions, New Ventures, Inc
701 E Franklin St, Ste 712
Richmond, VA 23219
(804) 643-1081
Fax (804) 643-1085
www.nvnv.org

Community Business Partnership
7001 Loisdale Rd, Ste C
Springfield, VA 22150
(703) 768-1440
Fax (703) 768-0547
www.wbcnova.org

WASHINGTON

Community Capital Development
NW Women's Business Center
12199 Village Center Place
Chinook Building, Ste 203
Mulkiteo, WA 98275
(425) 423-9090
www.seattleccd.com

Washington Business Center
1437 South Jackson St, Ste 302
PO Box 22283
Seattle, WA 98747
(206) 324-4330
Fax (206) 325-4322
www.seattleccd.com

WEST VIRGINIA

Region 1 WorkForce Women's
Business Center
200 Value City Center Ste 601
Beckley, WV 25801
(304) 253-3145
www.westviginiawbc.org

WISCONSIN

Western Dairyland Economic
Opportunity Council, Inc.
418 Wisconsin Street
Independence, WI 54747
(800) 782-1063 x211
Fax (715) 985-3239
www.weterndairyland.org

Women's Business Initiative
Corporation
2300 S Park Street
Madison, WI 53713
(608) 257-5450
www.wwbic.com

National Association of Women Business Owners (NAWBO)
NAWBO National Headquarters
8405 Greensboro Drive Ste 800
Mclean, VA 22102
(800) 55-NAWBO
www.nawbo.org
national@nawbo.org

The National Association of Women Business Owners propels women entrepreneurs into economic, social and political spheres of power worldwide.

The National Association of Women Business Owners (NAWBO) is the only dues-based national organization representing the interests of all women entrepreneurs in all types of businesses. The organization currently has over 75 chapters.

NAWBO traces its origins to a small group of Washington, DC businesswomen who began meeting informally in the Spring of 1974 to talk about mutual experiences, exchange information and develop business skills. Recognizing the value of the group, they incorporated as the National Association of Women Business Owners on July 5, 1975. Two years later they began recruiting members from across the country, and in 1978 the first chapters were formed.

In principle and in practice the National Association of Women Business Owners (NAWBO) values and seeks a diverse and inclusive membership. NAWBO shall seek full participation in the organization by all women business owners regardless of race, creed, age, sexual orientation, national origin, or disability. NAWBO's goal is to fully represent the diverse make-up of the women business owner community through increased representation within ethnic and minority communities and to expand access to leadership opportunities.

NAWBO Local Chapters

ARKANSAS
NAWBO Central Arkansas Chapter
813 West 3rd St
Little Rock, AR 72201
(501) 244-2332
www.canawbo.org

ARIZONA
NAWBO Phoenix Metro Chapter
6909 W Ray Road, Building 15
Chandler, AZ 85226
(480) 282-5176
www.nawbophx.org

NAWBO Sedona- Verde Valley
PO Box 3914
Sedona, AZ 86340
www.nawbosvv.org

NAWBO Greater Tucson Chapter
P O Box 31927
Tucson, AZ 85751
(520) 326-2926
Fax (520) 326-2927
www.nawbotucson.org

ALABAMA
NAWBO Birmingham
1900 International Park Drive
Birmingham, AL 35243
(205) 970-6316 ext 324
www.nawbobirminham.org

CALIFORNIA
NAWBO California-a consortium of all CA chapters
P O Box 1714
Tustin, CA 92781
(888) NAWBO-CA
Fax (714) 730-4019
www.nawbo-ca.org

NAWBO Inland Empire
P.O. Box 1501
Upland, CA 91785
www.nawbo-ie.org

NAWBO Los Angeles Chapter
900 Wilshire Blvd, Ste 404
Los Angeles, CA 90017
(213) 622-3200
Fax (213) 622-6659
www.nawbola.org

NAWBO Orange County Chapter
1240 N Jefferson Street, Ste G
Anaheim,CA 92807
(714) 630-2983
Fax (714) 632-5405
www.nawbo-oc.org

NAWBO Sacramento Valley
PO Box 189222
Sacramento, CA 95818
(916) 202-7294
Fax (916) 452-8884
www.nawbo-sac.org
admin@nawbo-sac.org

NAWBO Santa Barbara
3463 State Street, #231
Santa Barbara, CA 93105
(805) 880-0457
www.nawbo-sb.org

NAWBO San Diego
3990 Old Town Ave, Ste C100
San Diego, CA 92110
(877) 866-2926
Fax (619) 299-5966
www.nawbo-sd.org
info@nawbo-sd.org

NAWBO San Francisco Bay Area Chapter- c/o Barbara Mark, PhD
Full Circle Institute
2325 Third Street, Ste 337
San Francisco, CA 94107
(415) 333-2130
www.nawbo-sf.org
info@nawbo-sf.org

NAWBO Silicon Valley Chapter
PO Box 2696
Santa Clara, CA 95055-2696
(408) 257-3857
www.nawbo-sv.org
info@nawbo-sv.org

NAWBO Ventura County
5330 Derry Ave
Agoura Hills, CA 91301
(877) 629-2682
www.nawbovc.org
info@nawbovc.org

COLORADO

NAWBO Denver
PO Box 21552
Denver, CO 80221
(303) 758-0838
Fax (303) 758-7399
www.nawbodenver.com
info@nawbodenver.com

CONNECTICUT

NAWBO Connecticut
(203) 789-2437
www.nawboct.org
membership@nawboct.org

DELAWARE

NAWBO Delaware Chapter
4657 Greenville Station
Greenville, DE 19807-4657
(302) 355-9945
www.nawbodelaware.org
info@nawbodelaware.org

FLORIDA

NAWBO Greater Miami
(305) 271-6797
www.nawbomiami.org
info@nawbomiami.org

NAWBO Lakeland Metro Chapter
PO Box 5028
Lakeland, FL 33807
(863) 646-7166
www.nawbolakelandmetro.org

NAWBO Orlando
PO Box 536893
Orlando, FL 32803-6893
(407) 246-4646
www.nawboOrlando.org

NAWBO Ft Lauderdale/Broward Co Chapter
825 NW 61st St
Ft Lauderdale, FL 33309-2037
(954) 767-8600
www.nawbo-ftl.org

GEORGIA

NAWBO Atlanta
1188 Dorby Park Dr.
Atlanta, GA 30319
(770) 433-1166
Fax (404) 745-8045
www.nawbo-atlanta.org

IDAHO

NAWBO Boise
8428-A W Fairview Ave
Boise, ID 83704
(208) 322-9299
Fax (208)685-2915
www.nawboboise.org

ILLINOIS

NAWBO Central Illinois
(309) 691-0761
www.nawbo-cil.org

NAWBO Chicago Area Chapter
216 W Jackson Blvd Ste 625
Chicago, IL 60606
(312) 750-1200
Fax (312) 750-1203
www.nawbochicago.org
info@nawbochicago.org

NAWBO Springfield
(217) 529-0454
www.springfieldnawbo.com

INDIANA

NAWBO Indiana
2126 Meridian Street, Ste 220
Indianapolis, IN 46202
(317) 573-2222
Fax (317) 245-9343
www.nawboindy.org

IOWA

NAWBO Central Iowa
(515) 984-9500
www.nawbo-ci.org

KENTUCKY

NAWBO Lexington Chapter
PO Box 1806
Lexington, KY 40588
(859) 296-2800
www.lexnawbo.org

NAWBO Louisville Chapter
Louisville, KY 40202
(502) 585-4099
www.nawbolouisville.org

LOUISIANA
NAWBO New Orleans
4227 Canal Street
New Orleans, LA 70119
(504) 831-1813
www.nawbo-no.org

MAINE
NAWBO-Bangor
Bangor, ME
(207) 947-2731
www.nawbobangor.com

MARYLAND
NAWBO Baltimore
4404 Silverbrook Ln, Ste E-204
Owings Mills, MD 21117
(410) 876-0502
Fax (410) 654-9734
www.nawbomaryland.org
info@nawbomaryland.org

MASSACHUSETTS
NAWBO Boston
12 Alfred Street, Ste 300
Woburn, MA 01810
(781) 897-1787
www.nawboboston.com

MICHIGAN
NAWBO Greater Detroit Chapter
26677 West 12 Mile Road
Southfield, MI 48034
(248) 479-0331
www.nawbogdc.org
info@nawbogdc.org

MINNESOTA
NAWBO Minnesota Chapter
(952) 929-7921
www.nawbo-mn.org
info@nawbo-mn.org

MISSOURI
NAWBO Kansas City
(913) 317-6611 ext 3515
www.nawbo-kc.org

NAWBO Greater St Louis
PO Box 6925
St Louis, MO 63123
(314) 645-6465
www.nawbostl.org
info@nawbostl.org

NORTH CAROLINA
NAWBO Charlotte
1800 Camden Road Ste 107 #44
Charlotte, NC 28203
(704) 367-3454
Fax (814) 371-1499
www.nawbocharlotte.org
nawbo@nawbocharlotte.org

NAWBO Greater Raleigh Chapter
PO Box 30337
Raleigh, NC 27622
(919)-424-8248
www.nawbo-raleigh.org

NEW JERSEY
NJAWBO State Headquarters
Windsor Business Park Bldg 4B
186 Princeton Hightstown Road
West Windsor, NJ 08550
(609) 799-5101
Fax (609) 799-5141
www.njawbo.org
njawbo@njawbo.org

If you are located in these areas, please join NAWBO South Jersey:

Atlantic
Burlington
Camden
Cape May
Cumberland
Glouchester
Mercer-the southern third-Trenton
Salem

NAWBO South Jersey
(856) 488-0798
www.nawbosouthjersey.org
info@nawbosouthjersey.org

NAWBO North and Central Jersey
(732) 223-1692
www.nawbocentraljersey.org

NEW MEXICO
NAWBO Northern New Mexico
PO Box 30887
Albuquerque, NM 87190
(505) 922-1973
Fax (505) 299-9443
www.nawbonm.org

NEW YORK
NAWBO New York City
171 Madison Ave, Ste 1308
New York, NY 10016
(212) 252-1100
Fax (212) 252-1800
www.nawbonyc.org
info@nawbonyc.org

NAWBO Long Island
1225 Franklin Ave suite 325
Garden City, NY 11530
(516) 466-3470
www.nawboli.org
info@nawboli.org

NAWBO Greater Rochester
P O Box 369
Penfield, NY 14526
(585) 319-0004
Fax (585) 486-5574
www.nawborochester.org
grcnawbo@nawborochester.net

NAWBO Buffalo/Niagara
PO Box 917
Williamsville, NY 14221
(716) 580-1135
www.nawbonf.org

OHIO
NAWBO Cleveland
5910 Harper Road
Suite 102
Cleveland OH 44139-1835
(440) 914-9262
Fax (440) 914-0366
www.nawbocleveland.org
mailbox@nawbocleveland.org

NAWBO Columbus
(614) 793-2272
www.nawbocolumbusohio.com

NEVADA
NAWBO Southern Nevada
PO Box 96355
Las Vegas, NV 89193
(888) 736-1519 ext 87
www.nawbolasvegas.org

OKLAHOMA
NAWBO Central Oklahoma
P O Box 22811
Oklahoma City OK 73123-1811
(405) 205-5557
www.nawbook.org
nawbo@nawbook.org

NAWBO Tulsa
(918) 582-2326
www.nawbotulsa.org
nawbo@tulsa.com

PENNSYLVANIA
NAWBO Greater Philadelphia Chapter
1231 Highland Ave
Fort Washington, PA 19034
(215) 628-3875
Fax (215) 628-9839
www.nawbophila.org
nawbophi@barrpino.com

NAWBO Pittsburgh
700 River Avenue
Pittsburgh, PA 15212
(412) 628-5048
www.nawbopittsburgh.org
nawbo@nawbopittsburgh.org

NAWBO Northeast Pennsylvania
(570) 862-2849
www.nenawbo.com

TENNESSEE
NAWBO Nashville
PO Box 292283
Nashville, TN 37229-2283
(615) 664-6884
www.nashvillenawbo.com
info@nashvillenawbo.com

NAWBO Memphis
(901) 844-3738
www.nawbomemphis.org
info@nawbomemphis.org

NAWBO Chattanooga and Tri-State Area
PO Box 23874
Chattanooga, TN 37422
(423) 886-8367
www.chanawbo.org

TEXAS
NAWBO Dallas / Fort Worth
P O Box 361
Haslet, TX 76052
(214) 428-7475
www.nawbotx.org
info@nawbotx.org

NAWBO Houston
6124 Highway 6 North, #118
Houston, TX 77084
(281) 494-1010
www.nawbohouston.org
info@nawbohouston.org

NAWBO San Antonio
PO Box 460724
San Antonio, TX 78246-0724
(210) 408-1699
Fax (210) 408-1799
www.nawbo-sa.org

UTAH
NAWBO Salt Lake
PO Box 526095
Salt Lake City, UT 84152-6095
(801) 487-4600
Fax (801) 532-4819
www.nawboslc.org
office@nawboslc.org

VIRGINIA
NAWBO Northern Virginia
2308 Mt Vernon Ave #748
Alexandria, VA 222301
(703) 635-7773
Fax (703) 683-0018
www.nawbonova.org
info@nawbonova.org

NAWBO Richmond Area
PO Box 3211
Glen Allen, VA 23058-3211
(804) 346-5644
Fax (804) 360-2386
www.nawborichmond.org
info@nawborichmond.org

NAWBO Southeast Virginia
(757) 361-5003
www.nawboseva.org

WASHINGTON
NAWBO Inland Northwest Chapter
(509) 327-7331
www.nawbonw.org

WISCONSIN
NAWBO Greater Milwaukee
P O Box 26124
Wauwatosa, WI53226
(414) 358-9290
www.nawbo-gm.org
info@nawbo-gm.org

NAWBO Greater Madison Chapter
2110 Luann Lane
Madison, WI 53713
(608) 442-1924
www.nawbomadison.org
nawboinfo@nawbomadison.org

Washington D.C.
NAWBO- Nation's Capital
2308 Mount Vernon Avenue #748
Alexandria, VA 22301
(703) 683-8655
www.dealsinheels.com
info@nawbogreaterdc.org

National Women Business Owners Corporation (NWBOC)--Certifying Organization of NAWBO
1001 W Jasmine Dr, Ste G
Lake Park, FL 33403
(800) 675-5066
Fax (561) 881-7364
www.nwboc.org
info@nwboc.org

NWBOC, a national 501(c)(3) not-for-profit corporation, was established to increase competition for corporate and government contracts through implementation of a pioneering economic development strategy for women business owners. NWBOC provides a national certification program for women owned and controlled business as an alternative to the multiple state and local certifications required by many public and private sector agencies. Over 100 private and public agencies now accept NWBOC certification. (See Section 12: Certifying Organizations).

Center for Women's Business Research--Sister Organization of NAWBO
1760 Old Meadow Road, Ste 500
McLean, VA 22102
(703) 556-7162
Fax (703) 506-3266
www.womensbusinessresearch.org
info@womensbusinessresearch.org

Mission Statement
The Women's Business Enterprise National Council (WBENC) is dedicated to advancing the success of certified women's business enterprises, government agencies and corporate members in partnership with its affiliated women's business organizations.

The Center for Women's Business Research is a non-profit research organization, is the premier source of information on women business owners and their firms worldwide. Its mission is to support the growth of women business owners and their enterprises by conducting research, sharing information and increasing knowledge. It provides original, ground breaking research to document the economic and social contributions of women-owned firms; consulting and public relations services to maximize the benefits of this knowledge; and leadership development for women who own growing enterprises. Center for Women's Business Research provides corporations, government policy makers, educators, organizations, the media, and individuals with the intelligence they need to strengthen their support of women business owners.

Women's Business Enterprise National Council (WBENC)
1120 Connecticut Ave NW, Ste 1000
Washington, DC 20036
(202) 872-5515
Fax (202) 872-5505
www.wbenc.org
info@wbenc.org

The Women's Business Enterprise National Council (WBENC), founded in 1997, is the nation's leading advocate of women-owned businesses as suppliers to America's corporations. It also is the largest third-party certifier of businesses owned and operated by women in the United States. WBENC works to foster diversity in the world of commerce with programs and policies designed to expand opportunities and eliminate barriers in the marketplace for women business owners. WBENC works with representatives of corporations to encourage the utilization and expansion of supplier/vendor diversity programs.

Dedicated to enhancing opportunities for women's business enterprises, WBENC works in partnership with women's business organizations located throughout the country to provide a national standard of certification for women-owned businesses. The organization also provides its corporate members and certified women's business enterprises (WBEs) with access to a range of B2B sourcing tools including, an Internet database that contains information on certified women's businesses for purchasing managers nationwide. WBENC is a resource for the more than 700 US companies and government agencies that rely on the WBENC certification as an integral part of their supplier diversity programs.

Through its benchmarking surveys and ongoing interaction with certified women's business enterprises, WBENC has become the nation's leading source of information on trends in supplier diversity programs for WBEs at US companies and government agencies. WBENC also promotes best practices in supplier diversity through the annual selection of "America's Top Corporations for Women's Business Enterprises."

WBENC prepares and provides its partner organizations with on-site training and educational materials detailing certification procedures and program management. WBENC's research projects and surveys, primarily of CEOs and corporate procurement decision-makers, help to identify impediments to doing business and suggest "best practices" to maximize WBE opportunities and expand and enhance supplier diversity programs. The "Balanced Scorecard for WBE Program Process Improvement" assists WBENC corporate members in self evaluating their WBE programs.

PRIVATE SECTOR WOMEN-OWNED BUSINESS RESOURCES

American Business Women's Association
9100 Ward Pkwy
PO Box 8728
Kansas City, MO 64114-0728
(800) 228-0007
Fax (816) 361-4991
www.abwa.org
abwa@abwa.org

Asian Women in Business
42 Broadway, Ste 1748
New York, NY 10004
(212) 868-1368
www.awib.org
info@awib.org

Association of Women Professionals
P O Box 5560
Chicago, IL 60680
(773) 221-7250
www.awoman.org

Business & Professional Women USA
1620 Eye Street NW, Ste 210
Washington, DC 20006
(202) 293-1100
Fax (202) 861-0298
www.bpwusa.org

Catalyst Inc.
120 Wall St, 5th Fl
New York, NY 10005
(212) 514-7600
(212) 514-8470
www.catalystwomen.org
info@catalystwomen.org

Count Me In
(212) 245-1245
www.countmein.org
info@count-me-in.org

Digital Women
3800 Boquillas CR
Granbury, TX 76048
(817) 914-4665
www.digital-women.com

eWomenNetwork, Inc
14900 Landmark Blvd, Ste 540
Dallas, TX 75254
(972) 620-9995
Fax (972) 720-9995
www.ewomennetwork.com
info@ewomennetwork.com

Executive Women International
515 South 700 East Suite 2A
Salt Lake City, Utah 84102
(801) 355-2800
Fax (801) 355-2852
www.executivewomen.org
ewi@executivewomen.org

National Association for Female Executives
P O Box 3052
Langhome, PA 19047
(800) 927-6233
www.nafe.com
members@nafe.com

National Association of Negro Business and Professional Women's Clubs
1806 New Hampshire Ave NW
Washington, DC 20009
(202) 483-4206
www.nanbpwc.org
info@nanbpwc.org

National Association of Women in Construction
327 S Adams St
Fort Worth, TX 76104
www.nawic.org
nawic@nawic.org

National Education Center for Women in Business (NECWB)
Seton Hill University's E Magnify
P O Box 389F, Seton Hill University
Greensburg, PA 15601
(724) 830-4625
Fax (724) 834-7131
www.e-magnify.com

National Foundation for Women Business Owners (NFWBO)
Center for Women's Business Research
1760 Old Meadow Road, Ste. 500
McLean, VA 22102
(703) 556-7162
Fax (703) 506-3266
www.nfwbo.org
info@womensbusinessresearch.ORG

National Institute for Women in Trades, Technology, and Science
1150 Ballena Blvd, Ste 102
Alameda, CA 94501-3682
(510) 749-0200
Fax (510) 749-0500
www.iwitts.com

National Women's Business Council
409 Third St SW, Ste 210
Washington, DC 20024
(202) 205-3850
Fax (202) 205-6825
www.nwbc.gov

WomanOwned
(888) 663-9320
www.womanowned.com
info@womanowned.com

Women Construction Owners & Executives, USA
4401A Connecticut Avenue NW
Washington, DC 20008
(800) 788-3548
Fax (650) 551-5584
www.wcoeusa.org
info@wcoeusa.org

Women in Management, Inc
Box 1032
Dundee, IL 60118
(708) 386-0496
www.wimonline.org
nationalwim@wimonline.org

Women in Packaging, Inc
4290 Bells Ferry Road, Ste 106-17
Kennesaw, GA 30144-1300
(678) 594-6872
www.womeninpackaging.org
wpstaff@womeninpackaging.org

Women in Technology International
13351-D Riverside Drive #441
Sherman Oaks, CA 91423
(818) 788-9484
www.witi.com

Women's Center for Education and Career Advancement
11 Broadway, Ste 457
New York, NY 10004
(212) 964-8934
www.wceca.org

Women's Exchange, Inc
P O Box 660824
Birmingham, AL 35266-0824
(205) 967-0085
Fax (205) 967-0124
www.womens-exchange.com
info@womens-exchange.com

Women's Presidents Organization
155 E 55th St, Ste 4-H
New York, NY 10022
(212) 688-4114
Fax (212) 688-4766
www.womenpresidentsorg.com

Women's Venture Fund
New York Office
545 Eighth Avenue SE 17th floor
New York, NY 10018
(212) 563-0499
Fax (212) 868-9116
www.wvf-ny.org
info@wvf-ny.org

New Jersey Office
76 Clinton Avenue
Newark, NJ 07114
(877) 444-0934
Fax(212)868-9116
www.wvf-ny.org
info@wvf-ny.org

SECTION 12

CERTIFYING ORGANIZATIONS

The Small Business Administration's
Office of Small Disadvantaged Business Certification and Eligibility
409 Third St St, 8th Fl
Washington, DC 20416
(202) 619-1850

8(a) Business Development Program

www.sba.gov/8abd/

The SBA's 8(a) Business Development Program is strengthened and improved to be an effective business development vehicle. New regulations permit 8(a) companies to form beneficial teaming partnerships and allow Federal agencies to streamline the contracting process. New rules make it easier for non-minority firms to participate by proving their social disadvantage. The new Mentor-Protégé Program allows starting 8(a) companies to learn the ropes from experienced businesses. The task is to teach 8(a) and other small companies how to compete in the Federal contracting arena and how to take advantage of greater subcontracting opportunities available from large firms as the result of public-private partnerships.

The new and improved 8(a) Program has become an essential instrument for helping socially and economically disadvantaged entrepreneurs gain access to the economic mainstream of American society. Participation is divided into two phases over nine years: a four-year developmental stage and a five-year transition stage. In fiscal year 1998, more than 6,100 firms participated in the 8(a) Program and were awarded $6.4 billion in Federal contract awards.

Benefits of the Program

Participants can receive sole-source contracts, up to a ceiling of $3 million for goods and services and $5 million for manufacturing. While SBA helps 8(a) firms build their competitive and institutional know-how, the agency also encourages them to participate in competitive acquisitions.

Federal acquisition policies encourage Federal agencies to award a certain percentage of their contracts to SDBs. To speed up the award process, the SBA has signed Memorandums of Understanding (MOUs) with 25 Federal agencies allowing them to contract directly with certified 8(a) firms.

Recent changes permit 8(a) firms to form joint ventures and teams to bid on contracts. This enhances the ability of 8(a) firms to perform larger prime contracts and overcome the effects of contract bundling, the combining of two or more contracts together into one large contract.

Program goals require 8(a) firms to maintain a balance between their commercial and government business. There is also a limit on the total dollar value of sole-source contracts that an individual participant can receive while in the program: $100 million or five times the value of its primary SIC code. The overall program goal is to graduate firms that will go on to thrive in a competitive business environment.

To achieve this end, SBA district offices monitor and measure the progress of participants through annual reviews, business planning, and systematic evaluations. 8(a) participants may take advantage of specialized business training, counseling, marketing assistance, and high-level executive development provided by the SBA and its resource partners. They may also be eligible for assistance in obtaining access to surplus government property and supplies, SBA-guaranteed loans, and bonding assistance.

Eligibility Requirements
To qualify for the program, a small business must be owned and controlled by a socially and economically disadvantaged individual. Under the Small Business Act, certain presumed groups include African Americans, Hispanic Americans, Asian Pacific Americans, Native Americans, and Subcontinent Asian Americans. Other individuals can be admitted to the program if they show through a "preponderance of the evidence" that they are disadvantaged because of race, ethnicity, gender, physical handicap, or residence in an environment isolated from the mainstream of American society. In order to meet the economic disadvantage test, all individuals must have a net worth of less than $250,000, excluding the value of the business and personnel residence.
Successful applicants must also meet applicable size standards for small business concerns; be in business for at least two years; display reasonable success potential; and display good character. Although the two-year requirement may be waived, firms must continue to comply with various requirements while in the program.

Applying to the 8(a) Program
To apply to the 8(a) Program contact any SBA district office (see Section 2). For more information or questions, call the Division of Program Certification & Eligibility at (202) 205-6417.

National Minority Supplier Development Council (NMSDC)

1359 Broadway, Tenth Floor
New York, NY 10018
(212) 944-2430
www.nmsdc.org

The National Minority Supplier Development Council has standardized procedures to assure consistent and identical review and certification of minority-owned businesses. These businesses are certified by NMSDC's affiliate nearest to the company's headquarters.

A minority-owned business is a for-profit enterprise, regardless of size, physically located in the United States or its trust territories, which is owned, operated and controlled by minority group members. "Minority group members" are United States citizens who are Asian, Black, Hispanic and Native American. Ownership by minority individuals means the business is at least 51% owned by such individuals or, in the case of a publicly owned business, at least 51% of the stock is owned by one or more such individuals. Further, the management and daily operations are controlled by those minority group members.

Definition
For purposes of NMSDCs program, a minority group member is an individual who is a US citizen with at least 1/4 or 25% minimum (documentation to support claim of 25% required from applicant) of the following

Asian-Pacific	A US citizen whose origins are from Japan, China, Indonesia, Malaysia, Taiwan, Korea, Vietnam, Laos, Cambodia, the Philippines, Thailand, Samoa, Guam, the US Trust Territories of the Pacific or the Northern Marianas.
Asian-Indian	A US citizen whose origins are from India, Pakistan and Bangladesh.
Black	A US citizen having origins in any of the Black racial groups of Africa.
Hispanic	A US citizen of true-born Hispanic heritage, from any of the Spanish-speaking areas of the following regions: Mexico, Central America, South America and the Caribbean Basin only. Brazilians shall be listed under Hispanic designation for review and certification purposes.
Native American	A person who is an American Indian, Eskimo, Aleut or Native Hawaiian, and regarded as such by the community of which the person claims to be a part. Native Americans must be documented members of a North American tribe, band or otherwise organized group of native people who are indigenous to the continental United States and proof can be provided through a Native American Blood Degree Certificate (i.e., tribal registry letter, tribal roll register number).

NMSDC Growth Initiative

The Growth Initiative provides MBEs with the potential for substantial growth and with the opportunity to access equity capital, while retaining management and control, and the advocacy of NMSDC and its member corporations. The timely provision of this important tool is crucial if MBEs are to participate on an equal footing in the expanding national and global economies.

1. To qualify for NMSDC certification, an MBE is a for-profit enterprise, regardless of size, physically located in the United States or its trust territories, which is owned, operated and controlled by minority group members. "Minority group members" are United States citizens who are African-American, Hispanic-American, Native American, Asian-Pacific American and Asian-Indian American. Ownership by minority individuals means the business is at least 51% owned by such individuals. Further, the management and daily operations are controlled by those minority group members. This will not change.
2. This initiative affects only those NMSDC-certified firms that have an opportunity to accept equity capital from professional institutional investors, through the creation of a new class of non-voting stock.
3. Any exceptions to the 51% ownership policy would be made on a case-by-case basis; MBEs approved for this special certification will be tracked separately.
4. In these cases, a minority business may be certified as a minority business enterprise (MBE) if the minority owners own at least 30% of the economic equity* of the firm. This occurs when non-minority investors contribute a majority of the firm's risk capital (equity). Under this special circumstance, a business may be certified as a minority firm if the following criteria are met:
    a. Minority management/owners control the day-to-day operations of the firm.
    b. Minority management/owners retain a majority (no less than 51%) of the firm's "voting equity."
    c. Minority owner/s operationally control the board of directors (i.e., must appoint a majority of the board of directors).
5. In order to become certified as an MBE under the framework outlined in Section 4 above, the MBE's non-minority investor must be a "professional institutional investor" approved by the certifying committee. We define the term professional institutional investor to mean a firm that (a) is in the business of making equity investments (not managing businesses), and (b) manages more than $25 million in capital.
6. Given the complexity of the issues involved and the need for consistency in certification decisions, the National Minority Supplier Development Council (NMSDC) employs a national, rather than regional, certification committee for these purposes. Firms will be certified by a committee at the national level, in conjunction with members of the National Association of Investment Companies (NAIC), an industry association for investment companies that dedicate financial resources to investing in the ethnically diverse marketplace.
7. All NMSDC-certified MBEs, regardless of size, are eligible for this consideration.
8. This will not have any effect on the requirements of other nonprofit organizations or government agencies.

*The current requirement of 51% minority control severely restrains minority firms from expanding, by limiting non-minority secured financial investments to MBEs. To address this issue, there is a distinction made between "economic equity" and "voting equity". Economic equity refers to equity that gives the holder a residual claim on the firm's economic assets (i.e., it entitles the holder to a portion of the economic returns generated by the firm). Voting equity refers to the equity that gives the holder a vote for purposes of selecting a firm's board of directors.

Women's Business Enterprise National Council (WBENC)

1120 Connecticut Ave NW, Ste 1000
Washington, DC 20036
(202) 872-5515
Fax (202) 872-5505
www.wbenc.org

The WBENC certification for women-owned businesses is one of the most widely recognized and certifications in the nation. Accepted by over 700 major corporations across the country and a number of federal and government agencies, your WBENC certification will be an important marketing tool for expanding your company's visibility among decision makers in corporate supplier diversity and procurement.

Special programs and initiatives developed by WBENC also provide certified WBEs with added information, training and resources for growing their business opportunities in both the public and private sectors. Moreover, WBENC exclusive initiatives like WBENCLink, WEBuy, the Accelerator Program are designed especially for certified women's business enterprises.

Criteria for Certification

WBE (Women's Business Enterprise) is an independent business concern that is at least 51% owned and controlled by one or more women who are U.S. citizens or Legal Resident Aliens; whose business formation and principal place of business arein the US or its territories; and whose management and daily operation is controlled by one or more of the women owners.

National Women Business Owners Corporation (NWBOC)

1001 W Jasmine Dr, Ste G
Lake Park, FL 33403
(800) 675-5066
Fax (561) 881-7364
www.nwboc.org

The Women Business Owners Corporation has undertaken the National Certification Program as a public service for corporations, government agencies, and women business owners. NWBOC seeks to increase the ability of women business owners to compete for corporate and government contracts while at the same time decreasing the number of front operations participating in corporate and government outreach programs.
The NWBOC National Certification Program Standards and Procedures have been promulgated for use by NWBOC Consortium Partners in reviewing applications from businesses seeking to be certified as women-owned and -controlled. These Standards will also be used to evaluate the certification programs of potential Reciprocal Organizations.

NWBOC Certification Criteria

To be certified by a Consortium Partner, a female U.S. citizen must own and control the applicant as follows:
Ownership: A woman or women own(s) one of the following:
100% of the assets of a sole proprietorship;
at least 51% of the equity interests in a partnership; or
at least 51% of each of the classes of outstanding equity securities of a corporation.

Control: A woman or women controls one of the following:

- 100% of the control of a sole proprietorship;
- at least 51% of the control of a general partnership;
- woman owner is the general partner and, if there is more than one general partner, the managing general partner, of a limited partnership or limited liability partnership; or, the woman owner is entitled to appoint a majority of a corporate board of directors.

The NWBOC National Certification Program addresses only ownership and control of businesses. It is not an endorsement of applicant's goods and services.

California Public Utilities Commission (CPUC) M/WBE Clearinghouse

505 Van Ness Ave
San Francisco, CA 94102-3298
(415) 703-2782
Fax (415) 703-1758
www.cpuc.ca.gov

The verification process entails the thorough review of the completed Application Package with necessary supporting documents demonstrating evidence of ethnic and gender status as well as ownership, management and control. Any woman, minority, business enterprise which performs a service or produces a product used by the utility companies is encouraged to apply.

CPUC Definitions

Minority-Owned Business	A business enterprise that is at least 51% owned by one or more minority individuals, and whose management and daily operations are controlled by one or more minority individuals. Recognized minorities include Asian Americans, African Americans, Hispanic Americans and Native Americans among others.
Women-Owned Business	A business enterprise that is at least 51% owned by one or more women, and whose management and daily business operations are controlled by one or more women.

National Gay and Lesbian Chamber of Commerce (NGLCC)

1612 U Street NW, Ste 408
Washington, DC 20009
(202) 234-9181
Fax (202) 234-9185
www.nglcc.org
info@nglcc.org

NGLCC is the only national not-for-profit advocacy organization specifically dedicated to expanding the economic opportunities and advancements of the LGBT business community.
Seeking new opportunities for community advocacy, specifically in the economic arena, the NGLCC was founded as the exclusive organization for certification as an LGBT-owned business enterprise. The NGLCC is the direct link between Corporate America and LGBT businesses and entrepreneurs.

Certification Criteria

The NGLCC Supplier Diversity Initiative (SDI) offers businesses a tool to make connections and open doors with America's top corporations and each other. The SDI certifies Lesbian, Gay, Bisexual, and/or Transgender owned Business Enterprises (LGBTBEs) and works to provide opportunities for LGBTBEs to gain exposure within corporate procurement processes.

The NGLCC SDI offers certification to LGBTBEs, as well as a host of opportunities to enhance your business' visibility to corporations seeking to do business with LGBT suppliers. Corporations can search for certified LGBTBEs through our exclusive searchable LGBT supplier database, as well as meet face-to-face with potential suppliers at NGLCC SDI matchmaking events, which are held across the country throughout the year. Certified LGBTBEs may also be eligible for scholarship programs, mentorship and leadership training, and other business development tools to help your business grow.

Certification is an important marketing tool that can serve as a critical point of differentiation between your business and your competitors. Certification as a Lesbian, Gay, Bisexual, and/or Transgender owned Business Enterprise (LGBTBE) through the NGLCC Supplier Diversity Initiative (SDI) gives your business greater opportunities to develop and reach new potential corporate clients. The following criteria are required for certification as an LGBTBE. Your business must:

- Be at least fifty-one percent (51%) owned, operated, managed, and controlled by an LGBT persons or persons who are either U.S. citizens or lawful permanent residents
- Exercise independence from any non-LGBT business enterprise
- Have its principle place of business (headquarters) in the United States
- Have been formed as a legal entity in the United States

Department of Transportation (DOT) Certification

Office of Civil Rights
1200 New Jersey Avenue SE
Washington D.C. 20590
(202) 366-4754
www.dotr.ost.dot.gov

The Disadvantaged Business Enterprise (DBE) program is intended to remedy past and current discrimination against disadvantaged business enterprises, ensure a "level playing field" and foster equal opportunity in DOT-assisted contracts, improve the flexibility and efficiency of the DBE program, and reduce burdens on small businesses. This final rule replaces the former DBE regulation, which now contains only the rules for the separate DBE program for airport concessions, with a new regulation. The new regulation reflects President Clinton's policy to mend, not end, affirmative action programs. It modifies the Department's DBE program in light of developments in case law requiring "narrow tailoring" of such programs and last year's Congressional debate concerning the continuation of the DBE program.

Eligibility

An eligible Disadvantaged Business Enterprise (DBE) firm is one that is at least 51% owned and controlled by one or more socially and economically disadvantaged individuals. Also, the disadvantaged owner(s) personal net worth should not exceed the $750,000 threshold.

A firm must also be a small business concern as defined by the Small Business Administration's (SBA) Regulation at 13 CFR 121 and the Department's Regulation at 49 CFR Part 23 and 26, which provides for a cap of $16.6 million annual average gross receipts over a 3-year period for general construction firms.

Size standards for concessionaires doing business at airports differ from size standards of DBEs engaged in highway and transit related construction activities. 49 CFR 23 describes the size standards for airport concessions.

A joint venture can be certified as a DBE if the DBE partner meets the above criteria, shares in the ownership, control, management risk, and profits of the joint venture, and is responsible for a clearly defined portion of the work performed.

The Federal Highway Administration, Federal Transit Administration, and the Federal Aviation Administration uniformly apply DBE eligibility criteria for DOT-assisted projects. States and other local organizations and agencies may conduct their own certification or may rely on another recipient's certification. Many recipients rely on State DOT certifications. As presently structured, the recipient is always responsible for the certification of a Disadvantaged Business Enterprise firm.

Note: Eligibility criteria for concessionaires doing business at airports differ in size standards from DBEs engaged in highway, transit, or airport-related construction projects.

DBE Certification Appeals Program (DOT)
Certification is the Key to participating in the DBE Program.
The Director of the Departmental Office of Civil Rights has delegated responsibility to the External Policy and Program Development Division in FY 1999 to adjudicate appeals and other disputes relating to denials of DBE Certification by a transportation recipient. As such, the External Division investigates claims and issues final administrative decisions on an ongoing basis.

The External Policy and Program Development Division also conducts a number of other activities in support of this program. The staff provides training to State and local agencies on certification procedures and conducts outreach efforts to the community to inform individuals and businesses of their rights under the Department's Regulation, 49 CFR Parts 23 and 26.
The Department receives between 100 and 200 new appeals annually. The staff presently requires about 49 hours to adjudicate a case after receipt of the complete file. During the past 10 years, the Department adjudicated over 2000 certification appeals and third-party complaints.

The downward trend of appeals filed with the Department can be attributed to the External Division's participation with the Office of Small and Disadvantaged Business Utilization staff in its marketplace outreach program. If you need information on future visits and presentations, please call (202) 366-4754.

WEConnect Canada
85 Albert Street
Suite 1502
Ottawa, ON
K1P 6A4
www.weconnectcanada.org
info@weconnectcanada.org
Tel: (613) 230-3888 or toll-free (877) 857-3888
Fax: (613) 230-4999 or toll-free (877) 857-4999

Mission
WEConnect Canada delivers the leading international qualification or certification standard for women-owned businesses. We bring together the growing corporate and public sector demand for diverse supply chains with women's business enterprises based in Canada.
Certification as a Women Business Enterprise (WBE) by WEConnect is all about increasing your access to contract opportunities with corporations and governments in Canada and even internationally. Large corporations and organizations need a broad range of services, covering everything from technology to HR, event management and marketing. Certification verifies that your business is majority-owned (51%), managed and controlled by a

Canadian Aboriginal Minority Supplier Council (CAMSC)
95 Berkeley Street
Second Floor
Toronto, ON
M5A 2W8
Tel: (416) 941-0004
Fax: (416) 941-9282
www.camsc.ca
info@camsc.ca

CAMSC operates as a private sector-led, non-profit membership organization governed by a board of Directors; composed of major multinational corporations operating in Canada. The organization aims to boost economic development efforts and employment. The council is now accepting new corporate memberships from across Canada.

Mission

Deliver programs and processes to promote and facilitate procurement opportunities between major corporations in Canada and suppliers of all sizes owned and operated by Canadian Aboriginals and Minorities.

Certification Criteria

In order to be certified by CAMSC as an Aboriginal or visible minority supplier, an applicant must satisfy the following criteria:

- The applicant must be a for-profit enterprise
- The applicant must operate in Canada
- The applicant must be a Canadian citizen
- The applicant's business may be of any size
- The applicant must be able to operate as a supplier of products or services to other businesses; and
- The applicant's business must be owned and controlled by visible minorities or Aboriginal peoples.
- *Visible minority*: means persons other than Aboriginal peoples, who are non-Caucasian in race or non-white in color.
- *Aboriginal peoples*: means persons who are First Nation Inuit or Métis.
- Ownership by Aboriginal peoples, and/or visible minorities would mean that the business is at least 51% owned by such individuals. In the case of publicly owned businesses, at least 51% of the company's shares would have to be owned by one or more such individuals. Furthermore, the management and daily operations of these businesses must be controlled by visible minorities or Aboriginal people.

Local Regional Supplier Development Council Certification

The local councils of the NMSDC all offer certification to minority-owned businesses. Please see Section 14 for a list of the local councils.

State and City Certification

Each state and city may have different requirements for minority and women-owned business certification. Please see Section 13 for specific State and City M/WBE program information.

SECTION 13

CITY AND STATE DIVERSE SUPPLIER PROGRAMS

The 1989 Croson vs. City of Richmond court decision declared race-based set-aside programs unconstitutional - unless discrimination was documented. This decision resulted in the dismantling of many state and local diverse business utilization programs and, later, launched a series of disparity studies in an effort to prove past discrimination.

Because many jurisdictions are in various stages of determining the status of their set-aside programs, preparing disparity studies, and undergoing additional court challenges, it is recommended that you contact the individual jurisdiction with which you are concerned for current information.

CITY PROGRAMS

Listed below is a status report on the diverse supplier procurement programs of many major US cities. As court challenges cause changes and as disparity studies lead to new program initiatives, it is advisable to check with the jurisdiction for the most current program status.

ALASKA

Anchorage
Office of Equal Opportunity
Municipality of Anchorage
632 W 6th Ave, Ste 620
Anchorage, AK 99501
(907) 343-4890
www.muni.org

ALABAMA

Montgomery
Purchasing Division
103 North Perry Street
Montgomery, AL 36104
(334) 241-2610
www.montgomeryal.gov

ARIZONA

Phoenix
Community and Economic Development Department
200 W Washington, 20th Fl
Phoenix, AZ 85003-1611
(602) 262-5040
Fax (602-495-5097
www.phoenix.gov/ECONDEV/index.html

Tucson
Office of Equal Opportunity Programs (OEOP)
201 N. Stone, 3rd Floor
Tucson, AZ 85726
(520) 791-4593
Fax (520) 791-5140
www.ci.tuscon.az.us/eool

CALIFORNIA

Los Angeles
Minority Business Opportunity Center
City Hall
200 N Spring Street, 13th Floor
Los Angeles, CA 90012
(213) 978-0671
Fax (213) 978-0690
www.lamboc.org
lamboc@lacity.org

Port of Oakland
Contract Compliance Department
530 Water St
Oakland, CA 94607
(510) 627-1100
www.portofoakland.com

San Bernardino
Economic Development Agency
201 N "E" St, Ste 301
San Bernardino, CA 92401
(909) 663-1044
Fax (909) 888-9413
www.sbrda.org
info@sbrda.org
No formal program.

San Diego
Equal Opportunity Contracting
1200 Third Avenue, 2nd Floor
San Diego, CA 92101
(619) 235-5785
Fax (619) 235-5209
www.sandiego.gov/eoc

San Francisco
Human Rights Commission
25 Van Ness Ave,Room 800
San Francisco, CA 94102
(415) 252-2500
(415) 431-5764
www.sf-hrc.org

COLORADO

Denver
Office of Economic Development
201 W Colfax Avenue, 2nd Floor, Dept 1005
Denver, CO 80202
(720) 913-1999
www.milehigh.com

FLORIDA

Broward County
Office of Economic and Small Business Development
115 S Andrews Ave, Ste A640
Fort Lauderdale, FL 33301
(954) 357-6400
Fax (954) 357-6010
www.broward.org/smallbusiness

Jacksonville
City of Jacksonville
Equal Business Opportunity Office
214 Hogan Street N
Ed Ball Building, 8th Floor
Jacksonville, FL 32202
(904) 255-8827
www.coj.net

Miami
City of Miami Purchasing Department
444 SW Second Ave, 6th Fl
Miami, FL 33130
(305) 416-1900
www.ci.miami.fl.us/procurement

Orlando
Minority and Women Business Enterprise Dept.
City Hall, 5th Fl
400 S Orange Ave
Orlando, FL 32801
(407) 246-2623
www.cityoforlando.net/admin/mbe/

Tampa
Minority Business Development Office
306 E Jackson St
Tampa, FL 33602
(813) 274-5522
Fax (813) 274-5544
www.tampagov.net

GEORGIA

Albany
City of Albany, Dougherty County
Office of Small and Disadvantaged Business
222 Pine Ave, Ste 240
Albany, GA 31702
(229) 878-3151
Fax (229) 878-3158
http://production.albany.ga.us/SDBU/sdbu_index.htm

IOWA

Des Moines
Office of Economic Development
400 East 1st Street
Des Moines, IA 50309
(515) 283-4004
www.dmoed.org/

ILLINOIS

Chicago
Department of Procurement Services
City Hall, Rm 403
121 N LaSalle
Chicago, IL 60602
(312) 744-4900
Fax (312) 744-0010
www.cityofchicago.org/procurement

INDIANA

Indianapolis
Minority and Womens Business Enterprise Division
402 W Washington Street, Room W469
Indianapolis, IN 46204
(317) 232-3061
Fax (317) 233-6921
www.in.gov/idoa/2352.htm

KANSAS

Kansas City
Wyandotte Co. Purchasing Department
Procurement and Contract Compliance
701 N Seventh St, Ste 649
Kansas City, KS 66101
(913) 573-5440
www.wycokck.org

Topeka
City of Topeka
Contracts & Procurement
215 SE 7th St Room 358
Topeka, KS 66603-3914
(785) 368-3970
www.topeka.org/purchasing

KENTUCKY

Louisville County
Metro Louisville Human Relations Commission
410 W Chestnut St, Ste 300 A
Louisville, KY 40202
(502) 574-3631
Fax (502) 574-3577
www.louisvilleky.gov/humanrelations/

LOUISIANA

Baton Rouge
Department of Purchasing
300 North Boulevard Room 309
Baton Rouge, LA 70801
(225) 389-3259
Fax (225) 389-4841
www.brgov.com
purchasinginfo@brgov.com

New Orleans
Office of Economic Development
1340 Poydras St, Ste 1000
New Orleans, LA 70112
(504) 658-4200
Fax (504) 658-4238
www.cityofno.com

MARYLAND

Baltimore
Minority and Women's Business Development
City Hall, Rm 334
Baltimore, MD 21202
(410) 396-3818
Fax (410) 528-1671
www.ci.baltimore.md.us

MASSACHUSETTS

Boston
Small & Local Business Enterprise Office
Boston City Hall, One City Hall Square rm 717
Boston, MA 02201
(617) 635-4084
Fax (617) 635-3235
www.cityofboston.gov/slbe/default
slbe@cityofboston.gov

MICHIGAN

Detroit
Human Rights Department
2 Woodward Ave, Ste 1026
Detroit, MI 48226
(313) 224-4950
www.ci.detroit.mi.us/humanrights

Lansing
Purchasing Office
124 W Michigan Ave, 8th Floor
Lansing, MI 48933
(517) 483-4124
Fax (517) 483-4524
www.lansingmi.gov/finance/purchasing/index.jsp

MINNESOTA

Minneapolis
Small & Underutilized Business Program
350 South Fifth St, Rm 239
Minneapolis, MN 55415
(612) 673-2112
www.ci.minneapolis.mn.us/subp/gencon.asp

Saint Paul
Vendor Outreach Program
& CERT Program Coordinator
15 W Kellogg Blvd
280 City Hall/Court House
Saint Paul, MN 55102
(651) 266-8900
CERT Program: www.govcontracts.org
Saint Paul: www.stpaul.gov/index
cert@ci.stpaul.mn.us

MISSOURI

Kansas City
Human Relations Department
City Hall, 4th floor
414 E 12th St
Kansas City, MO 64106
(816) 513-1836
Fax (816) 513-1805
www.kcmo.org
jobs@kcmo.org

MISSISSIPPI

Jackson
Office of Economic Development
200 S President St, Ste 223
Jackson, MS 39205
(601) 960-1055
www.city.jackson.ms.us/cityhall/economdev.htm

NEBRASKA

Omaha
City of Omaha Human Rights and Relations Department
1819 Farnam St, Ste 502
Omaha, NE 68183
(402) 444-5055
www.cityofohmaha.org/humanrights

NEVADA

Las Vegas
Department of Finance & Business Services
Purchasing & Contracts Division
400 Stewart Ave
Las Vegas, NV 89101
(702) 229-6321
(702) 383-0769
www.lasvegasnevada.gov

NEW JERSEY

Newark
Office of Affirmative Action
920 Broad Street, Room B-25
Newark, NJ 07102
(973) 733-6400
www.ci.newark.nj.us

City of Trenton
City Hall
Economic Development Department
319 E State St
Trenton, NJ 08608
(609) 989-3504
www.trentonnj.org/
acarabelli@trentonnj.org

NEW MEXICO

Santa Fe
Economic Development Department
1100 St. Francis Dr. Ste 1060
Santa Fe, NM 87505
(800) 374-3061
www.edd.state.nm.us

NEW YORK

Albany
Office of Equal Employment Opportunity
City Hall, Rm 301
24 Eagle St.
Albany, NY 12207
(518) 434-5284
www.albanyny.org

New York
NY City Econonomic Development Corporation
Division of Economic & Financial Opportunity
110 Williams St, 2nd Floor
New York, NY 10038
(212) 619-5000
www.nycedc.com

NORTH CAROLINA

Charlotte
Office of Economic Development
600 East 4th Street
Charlotte, NC 28232
(704) 432-1395
www.charmeck.org/Departments/Economic+Development

Raleigh
Administrative Services Department
Business Assistance Program Manager
222 W Hargett St, Rm 302
Raleigh, NC 27601
(919) 996-3840
www.raleigh-nc.org/adminservices/mwbe/

NORTH DAKOTA

Bismarck
City Administration
221 N Fifth St
Bismarck, ND 58501-4208
(701) 355-1300
Fax (701) 222-6470
www.bismarck.org

OHIO

Cincinnati
Office of Contract Compliance / SBE Small Business Enterprise Program
805 Centennial Plaza, Ste 222
Cincinnati, OH 45202
(513) 352-3144
Fax (513) 352-3157
www.cincinnati-oh.gov

Cleveland
Office of Equal Opportunity
601 Lakeside Ave, City Hall Rm 335
Cleveland, OH 44114
(216) 664-4152
Fax (216) 664-3870
www.city.cleveland.oh.us

Columbus
Equal Business Opportunity Commission Office
109 N Front St, 4th Fl
Columbus, OH 43215-9020
(614) 645-4764
www.eboco.ci.columbus.oh.us

OKLAHOMA

Oklahoma City
Central Purchasing Division Office
Will Rogers Office Building
2401 N. Lincoln, Ste 116
Oklahoma City, OK 73105
(405) 522-0955
Fax (405) 521-4475
www.ok.gov/dcs/central_purchasing

Tulsa
City of Tulsa
Human Rights Department
175 East 2nd Street, One Technology Center 8th Fl.
Tulsa, OK 74103
(918) 596-7818
www.cityoftulsa.org/community-programs/
humanrights.aspx

OREGON

Portland
Bureau of Purchases
1120 SW Fifth Ave, Rm 750
Portland, OR 97204-1913
(503) 823-6855
Fax (503) 823-6865
www.portlandonline.com

PENNSYLVANIA

Harrisburg
Mayor's Office of Economic Development
City Government Center
10 N Second, Ste 405
Harrisburg, PA 17101
(717) 255-3027
Fax (717) 222-6432
www.harrisburgcity.com/government/moed

Pittsburgh
Equal Opportunity Review Commission
414 Grant St, Rm 328
Pittsburgh, PA 15219
(412) 255-8804
www.city.pittsburgh.pa.us/eorc/

SOUTH CAROLINA

Columbia
SC Statewide Minority Business Development Center
1515 Richland St
Columbia, SC 29201
(803) 779-5905
(803) 779-5915
www.scmbec.com

TEXAS

Austin
Dept of Small & Minority Business Resources
4201 Ed Bluestein Blvd.
Austin, TX 78721
(512) 974-7600
Fax (512) 974-7601
www.cityofaustin.org/smbr

Dallas
Business Development & Procurement Services
1500 Marilla, Rm 3F North
Dallas, TX 75201
(214) 670-3326
Fax (214) 670-4793
www.dallascityhall.com

Fort Worth
M/WBE Office
908 Monroe Street 3rd Floor
Fort Worth, TX 76102
(817) 392-7540
Fax (817) 392-7328
www.fortworthgov.org/mwbe

Houston
Affirmative Action & Contract Compliance Division
PO Box 1562
901 Bagby
Houston, TX 77251
(713) 837-0311
www.houstontx.gov/aacc

UTAH

Salt Lake City
Purchasing Department
P O Box 145455
City and County Building Rm 235
Salt Lake City, UT 84111
(801) 535-7661
www.slcgov.com

VIRGINIA

Alexandria
Office of Human Rights
421 King Street, Ste 400
Alexandria, VA 22314
(703) 746-3140
Fax (703) 838-4976
http://alexandriava.gov/humanrights

Norfolk
Office of the Purchasing Agent
Granby Municipal Bldg
401 Monticello Ave, Rm. 420
Norfolk, VA 23510
(757) 664-4787
Fax (757) 664-4018
www.norfolk.gov/purchasing/

Richmond
Office of Minority Business Development (OMBD)
900 E Broad St, 9th Fl
Richmond, VA 23219
(804) 646-5947
Fax (804) 646-0136
www.richmondgov.com/MBD

Virginia Beach
Department of Economic Development
222 Central Park Ave, Ste 1000
Virginia Beach, VA 23462
(757) 385-6464
www.yesvirginiabeach.com
ecdev@vbgov.com

WISCONSIN

Madison
Division of Affirmative Action
City County Bldg, Rm 523
210 Martin Luther King Jr Blvd
Madison, WI 53703
(608) 266-4910
www.cityofmadison.com `

County of Milwaukee
Community Business Development Partners (CBDP)
2711 W Wells St
City Campus, Room 830
Milwaukee, WI 53208
(414) 278-4803
www.milwaukeecounty.org

Milwaukee
Emerging Business Enterprise Program
200 E Wells St
City Hall, Rm 606
Milwaukee, WI 53202
(414) 286-5553
Fax (414) 286-8752
www.city.milwaukee.gov

WYOMING

Cheyenne
Department of Purchasing
2101 O'Neil Ave Room 104
Cheyenne, WY 82001
(307) 637-6345
www.cheyennecity.org

STATE PROGRAMS

Listed below are offices with responsibility for state diverse supplier procurement programs. Some states have set-aside programs for DBE participation in state contracts; others have established voluntary goals; others have no formal program.

NOTE: Most states have a DOT goal of 10%

ALABAMA
State Office of Minority Business Enterprise
ADECA
401 Adams Ave Suite 410
PO Box 5690
Montgomery, AL 36103
(334) 242-5100
Fax (343) 242-5099
www.adeca.alabama.gov

ALASKA
Alaska Department of Transportation & Public Facilities
Civil Rights Office
2200 E 42nd Ave
PO Box 196900
Anchorage, AK 99519-6900
(907) 269-0851
www.dot.state.ak.us/cvlrts

ARKANSAS
Arkansas Economic Development Commission
Small and Minority Business Division
One Capitol Mall
Little Rock, AR 72201
(501) 682-1121 or (800) ARKANSAS
www.aekansasedc.com

ARIZONA
Arizona Department of Commerce
Small Business Services
1700 W Washington, Ste 600
Phoenix, AZ 85007
(602) 771-1100
www.azcommerce.com

CALIFORNIA
Office of Small Business & Disabled Veteran Business Enterprise Services (OSDS)
Department of General Services
707 3rd St, 2nd floor
West Sacramento, CA 95605
(916) 375-4400 or (800) 559-5529
www.pd.dgs.ca.gov (click on Small Business)

COLORADO
Minority Business Office
Office of Economic Development & Intl Trade
1625 Broadway, Ste 2700
Denver, CO 80202
(303) 892-3840
Fax (303) 892-3848
www.state.co.us/oed/mbo

CONNECTICUT
Department of Administrative Services-Procurement
Meg Yetishefskey, Director
165 Capitol Avenue
Hartford, CT 06106
(860) 713-5095
Fax (860) 713-7484
www.das.state.ct.us

DELAWARE
Delaware Department of Transportation
Disadvantaged Business Enterprise
Richard Rexrode
800 Bay Road
PO Box 778
Dover, DE 19903
(302) 760-2035
Fax (302)739-2254
www.deldot.net/static/business/dbe/

DISTRICT OF COLUMBIA
Office of Local Business Development
441 Fourth St NW, Ste 970N
Washington, DC 20001
(202) 727-3900
Fax (202) 724-3786
http://olbd.dc.gov/olbd/

FLORIDA
Office of Supplier Diversity
Torey Alston, Executive Director
4050 Esplande Way, Ste 380I
Tallahassee, FL 32399-0950
(850) 487-0915
Fax (850) 922-6852
www.osd.dms.state.fl.us

GEORGIA
Department of Administrative Services
200 Piedmont Ave, Ste 1804, West Tower
Atlanta, GA 30334
(404) 656-5514
Fax: (404) 651-9595
www.doas.state.ga.us

IDAHO
Department of Administration
Purchasing
650 West State Street
PO Box 83720
Boise, ID 83720-0075-5569
(208) 327-7456
Fax (208) 327-7320
http://adm.idaho.gov

ILLINOIS
Illinois Department of Central Management Services
Business Enterprise Program
100 W Randolph St, Suite 4-100
Chicago, IL 60601
(312) 814-4190 or (800) 365-9206
www.sell2.illinois.gov/BEP/Business_Enterprise.htm

INDIANA
Department of Administration
Minority & Women's Business Enterprises Division
402 W Washington St, Ste W469
Indianapolis, IN 46204
(317) 232-3061
Fax: (317) 233-6921
mwbe@idoa.in.gov
www.in.gov/idoa/minority

IOWA
Targeted Small Business Finance Manager
Department of Economic Development
200 E Grand Ave
Des Moines, IA 50309
(515) 242-4700
www.iowalifechanging.com

KANSAS
Office of Minority & Women Business Development
Kansas Department of Commerce
Business Development Division
1000 SW Jackson, Ste 100
Topeka, KS 66612-1354
(785) 296-3481
Fax (785) 296-5055
www.kansascommerce.com

KENTUCKY
Kentucky Cabinet for Economic Development
Small & Minority Business
Old Capitol Annex - 300 West Broadway
Frankfort, KY 40601
(502) 564-7140 or (800) 626-2930
www.thinkkentucky.com/kyedc/busstart.aspx

LOUISIANA
Department of Economic Development
Mayor's Office of Small & Emerging Business Development
1051 N Third St
Baton Rouge, LA 70802
(800) 450-8115
Fax (225) 342-3000
www.lded.state.la.us

MAINE
Maine Dept of Transportation/Civil Rights
Office of Civil Rights
16 State House Station
Augusta, ME 04333-0016
(207) 624-3401
www.maine.gov/mdot/disadvantaged-business-enterprises/dbe-home.php

MARYLAND
State of Maryland
Governor's Office of Minority Affairs
6 St Paul Street, Ste 1502
Baltimore, MD 21202
(410) 767-8232 or (877) 558-0998
www.mdminoritybusiness.com

Maryland Department of Transportation
Office of Minority Business Enterprise
7201 Corporate Center Drive
Hanover, MD 21076
(410) 865-1142 or (888) 713-1414
www.marylandtransportation.com

MASSACHUSETTS
State Office of Minority & Women Business Assistance (SOMWBA)
10 Park Plaza Ste 3740
Boston, MA 02116
(617) 973-8692
Fax (617) 973-8637
www.somwba.state.ma.us
wsomwba@state.ma.us

MICHIGAN
Michigan Economic Development Corporation
Small Business Services
300 N Washington Sq
Lansing, MI 48913
(888) 522-0103
www.michiganadvantage.org

MINNESOTA
Department of Administration
Materials Management Division
112 Administration Bldg
50 Sherburne Ave
St Paul, MN 55155
(651) 296-2600
Fax (651) 297-3996
www.mmd.admin.state.mn.us/

MISSISSIPPI
Mississippi Development Authority
Minority & Small Business Development Division
PO Box 849
501 N West St
Jackson, MS 39205
(601) 359-3448
Fax (601) 359-5290
www.mississippi.org

MISSOURI
State of Missouri
Office of Supplier and Workforce Diversity
Truman Sate Office Building
301 West High Street, rm 360
P O Box 809
Jefferson City, MO 65102
(573) 751-8130 or (877) 259-2963
www.oswd.mo.gov

MONTANA
Department of Transportation
Civil Rights Bureau
2701 Prospect Ave, PO Box 201001
Helena, MT 59620-1001
(406) 444-6337
www.mdt.mt.gov

NEBRASKA
Disadvantaged Business Enterprise Office
1500 Highway 2
PO Box 94759
Lincoln, NE 68509-4759
(402) 479-4531
Fax (402) 479-3728
www.dor.state.ne.us

NEVADA
State of Nevada
Purchasing Division
515 E Musser St, Ste 300
Carson City, NV 89701
(775) 684-0170
Fax: (775) 684-0188
www.purchasing.state.nv.us

NEW HAMPSHIRE
NH Department of Administrative Services
Bureau of Purchase & Property
State House Annex
25 Capitol St, Rm 102
Concord, NH 03301
(603) 271-2201
Fax (603) 271-2700
www.admin.state.nh.us/purchasing

NEW JERSEY
NJ Office of Economic Growth
Commerce, Economic Growth & Tourism
Commission
State House, 2nd floor
P O Box 001
Trenton, NJ 08625-0820
(866) 534-7789
www.nj.gov/njbusiness/contracting

NEW MEXICO
Purchasing Division
1100 St. Francis Dr. rm 2016
Santa Fe, NM 87505
(505) 827-0472
Fax (505) 827-2484
www.generalservices.state.nm.us/spd/
10% mixed M/WBE goals. No disparity study.

NEW YORK
Empire State Development Division of Minority &
Women's Business Development
30 S Pearl St
Albany, NY 12245
(800) 782-8369
www.nylovesmwbe.ny.gov

NORTH CAROLINA
Office for Historically Underutilized Businesses
1336 Mail Service Station
Raleigh, NC 27699
(919) 807-2330
www.doa.state.nc.us/hub

NORTH DAKOTA
ND Department of Transportation
608 E Blvd Ave
Bismark, ND 58505
(701)328-2500
www.dot.nd.gov/

OHIO
Department of Administrative Services
Equal Opportunity Division
30 E. Broad St., 18th floor
Columbus, OH 43215
(614) 466-8380
Fax (614) 728-5628
www.das.ohio.gov/eod

OREGON
Office of Minority, Women & Emerging Small Business
775 Summer Street NE, Ste 200
PO Box 14880
Salem, OR 97309-0405
(503) 986-0073
Fax (503) 373-7041
www.cbs.state.or.us/OMWESB/

PENNSYLVANIA
Bureau of Minority & Women Business Opportunities
Department of General Services
Room 611, North Office Bldg
Harrisburg, PA 17125
(717) 783-3119
Fax (717) 787-7052
www.dgs.state.pa.us/bcabd/

RHODE ISLAND
Minority Business Enterprise Compliance Office
One Capitol Hill, 2nd Fl
Providence, RI 02908
(401) 574-8670
www.mbe.ri.gov/

SOUTH CAROLINA
Governor's Office of Small and Minority Business Assistance
1205 Pendelton St, Ste 440-A
Columbia, SC 29201
(803) 734-5010
Fax: (803) 734-2498
www.govoepp.state.sc.us/osmba

SOUTH DAKOTA
Department of Transportation DBE Compliance
700 E Broadway Ave
Pierre, SD 57501
(605) 773-4906
www.sddot.com/operations/certified/dbe.asp

TENNESSEE
Governor's Office of Diversity Business Enterprise
William R Snodgrass Bldg./Tennessee Tower, 27th Fl
312 Rosa Parks Avenue
Nashville, TN 37243
(615) 253-4657 or (866) 894-5026
www.tennessee.gov/businessopp

Civil Rights Office
Small Business Development Office
505 Deaderick St, Ste 1800
James K Polk Bldg
Nashville, TN 37243
(615) 741-2848
www.tdot.state.tn.us/civil-rights/

Mid-South Minority Business Council (MMBC)
Uniform Certification Agency
158 Madison Avenue, Ste 300
Memphis, TN 38103
(901) 525-6512
www.mmbc-memphis.org

TEXAS
Office of Economic Development
Office of the Governor - Economic Development & Tourism
221 E 11th St
P O Box 12428
Austin, TX 78711
(800) 888-0511 or (512) 936-0100
www.governor.state.tx.us/ecodev/business_resources/sba

UTAH
State Offices of Ethnic Affairs
324 South & State St, Ste 500
Salt Lake City, UT 84111
(877) 488-3233, ext. 755
Fax: (801) 538-8678
http://ethnicoffice.utah.gov

VIRGINIA
The Commonwealth of Virginia
Department of Minority Business Enterprise
1111 E. Main St., Ste 300
Richmond, VA 23219
(804) 786-6585 or (888) 792-6323
www.dmbe.state.va.us

WASHINGTON
Office of Minority and Women's Business Enterprises
406 South Water Street
PO Box 41160
Olympia, WA 98504-7314
(866) 208-1064 or (360) 586-7079
www.omwbe.wa.gov

WEST VIRGINIA
Small Business Development Center
West Virginia Development Office
1900 Kanawha Blvd E, Bldg 6, Room 652
Charleston, WV 25305
(888) 982-7232 or (304) 558-2960
Fax (304) 558-0127
www.sbdcwv.org

WISCONSIN
Department of Commerce
Bureau of Minority Business Development
201 W Washington Ave, PO Box 7970
Madison, WI 53707-7970
(608) 267-9550
commerce.wi.gov
commbd@wisconsin.gov

WYOMING
Wyoming Department of Transportation
DBE Program
5300 Bishop Blvd.
Cheyenne, WY 82009
(307) 777-4456
www.dot.state.wy.us

SECTION 14

PRIVATE SECTOR

There are many supplier diversity development resources in the private sector.

Diversity Information Resources, Inc. (DIR)
2105 Central Ave NE
Minneapolis, MN 55418
(612) 781-6819
Fax (612) 781-0109
www.diversityinforesources.com
info@diversityinforesources.com

Diversity Information Resources (DIR) was founded in Minneapolis in 1968 by H. Peter Meyerhoff, a Honeywell aeronautics engineer, who sought to advance race relations by improving economic conditions for Blacks after the assassination of Dr. Martin Luther King, Jr. Meyerhoff and his wife were European Jews who managed to escape Hitler at the outset of World War II. Themselves victims of discrimination, they were motivated by Dr. King's death to launch the "Buy Black" directory - a 10 page directory of black-owned businesses. In 2001 DIR partnered with SupplierGATEWAY and developed an online Supplier Diversity Database Management Portal. The portal allows corporations access to certified minority and women-owned businesses, veteran, service-disabled veteran and HUBZone businesses, supplier registration, certification validation, diversity spend reporting and data cleansing. DIR also offers supplier diversity training through its Seminar: Building Strategic Phases of a Supplier Diversity Process.

Since 1968, DIR is widely regarded as this nation's most trusted and reliable organization for providing credible data on diverse suppliers. A board of directors representing major corporations sets policy and direction for the not-for-profit organization. DIR's mission is to be the global leader providing information resources that develops, influences and supports supplier diversity growth.

- The *Online Supplier Diversity Database Management Portal,* a dynamic portal with unlimited user access to an extensive database of certified M/WBE suppliers, Veteran, Service-Disabled Veteran and HUBZone businesses, extensive search capabilities, supplier registration, divers certification validation, data cleansing, business matchmaker, spend reporting, online posting, real time updates.

- *Supplier Diversity Seminars*: "Building Strategic Phases of a Supplier Diversity Process" provides practical help to establish or enhance Supplier Diversity programs. "Best Practices" in Supplier Diversity Strategies and Initiatives is a presentation-style seminar for supplier diversity professionals.

- The *National Minority and Women-Owned Business Directory*, a comprehensive list of certified minority & women-owned businesses with regional and/or national sales capabilities.

- *Purchasing People in Major Corporations* - Lists appoximately 700 corporate purchasing locations and indicates the supplier diversity manager, procurement or purchasing manager or buyer. Available in print or online.

- *Supplier Diversity Information Resource Guide* - Valuable, comprehensive information on supplier diversity. Features: information on minority/women business loans; legislative directives impacting City and State programs; annual calendar of supplier diversity events; City/State requirement and goals; addresses and contacts for Small Business Administration's Regional/District offices, Small Business Development Centers (SBDC), Minority Business Development Centers (MBDC), Regional Minority Supplier Development Councils, etc.; women's business resources; certifying organizations; minority/women business directories, and more.

DIVERSITY INFORMATION RESOURCES: SUPPLIER DIVERSITY SEMINARS

"Best Practices" in Supplier Diversity Strategies and Initiatives Seminar

DIR has sponsored the Best Practices in Supplier Diversity Strategies and Initiatives Seminar since 1995. The seminar is designed to share "Best Practices" with supplier diversity professionals on current trends and issues impacting supplier diversity programs. Presenters are supplier diversity practitioners with world-class supplier diversity programs.

TOPICS have included:

- CPO Roundtable
- Strategic Partnering
  - Internal and External Organizations
- Evaluating Program Metrics
  - Spend
  - Outreach Activities
  - Suppliers
- Supplier Data Management Tools
- Developing Diverse Suppliers
- Second Tier Process
  - RFP Evaluation
  - Contract Language
  - Tracking Spend
- Professional Development
  - Communication Skills
  - Strategic Thinking
- Government Subcontracting

Who Should Attend: Supplier Diversity Professionals, Public and Private Sector Supplier Diversity Professionals; Purchasing Managers and Buyers; Vice Presidents of Materials and Purchasing; Procurement Managers.

"Building Strategic Phases of a Supplier Diversity Process" Seminar

This seminar instructs corporations on how to implement supplier diversity programs and/or enhance existing programs.

Rationale

Companies establish supplier diversity programs for a variety of reasons. Most supplier diversity programs are driven by consumers, customers and compliance. Today's competitive global economy makes it essential that America utilize the strengths of all businesses.

Supplier Diversity Program Implementation

Establishing and enhancing a successful supplier diversity purchasing program involves integrating the supplier diversity program into the organization's total operations. The program should not be a "stand-alone" program or an appendage to the purchasing department. Rather, it should become an integral process tied to the organization's strategic plan. Diversity Information Resources recommends the following basic components be incorporated into a supplier diversity program:

1. **Support of the Chief Executive Officer**
   In order to achieve success, the supplier diversity program must have the unqualified endorsement and commitment of the CEO. A written policy statement must be effectively communicated company-wide.

2. **Assignment of Program Responsibility**
A Program Administrator should be assigned and resources allocated. Most supplier diversity programs are housed in the Purchasing Department because of its authority to solicit and award contracts. For larger companies with highly decentralized purchasing, it may be necessary to designate a supplier diversity manager to establish company-wide minority purchasing efforts. At a minimum, the responsibilities of the supplier diversity manager should include:

- Responsibility for overall implementation, guidance and monitoring of the program.
- Provide a central information resources bank about diverse suppliers.
- Identify purchasing opportunities for diverse suppliers.
- Monitor company-wide progress, including identification of problem areas or obstacles, and provide assistance to solve them.
- Coordinate internal and external reporting.
- Conduct in-house training for staff and diverse suppliers.
- Work with M/WBE support organizations.

3. **Development of a Strategic Plan**
The Supplier Diversity program should be a fully integrated part of the organization's strategic objectives. Key components of a Supplier Diversity Strategic Plan should include:

- Rationale for Supplier Diversity program
- Supplier Diversity Program Administrator job function
- Goals and objectives
- Reporting procedures
- Monitoring and evaluation systems
- Obtaining company-wide support
- Ongoing training (across all levels of corporation)

4. **Program Implementation Activities**
Once the program's Strategic Plan has been developed and approved, implementation procedures can be put in place. The listing below is a basic outline of the primary activities:

- Survey supplier base
- Determine certification/registration requirements
- Develop database of divese suppliers through supplier registration
- Develop list of purchasing opportunities
- Assign goals and objectives
- Develop Supplier Diversity Steering Committee which cuts across departmental lines
- Design incentives and awards program

5. **Outreach Activities**
Once the Supplier Diversity purchasing program is "up and running," the following areas should be addressed:

- Publicity (internal and external)
- External and internal website
- Brochure explaining supplier diverse program
- Trade fairs (in house and external)
- Networking activities with individuals/organizations involved in supplier diversity development

NOTE: For more information on seminar dates, locations and registration, contact Diversity Information Resources at (612) 781-6819 or visit the web site www.diversityinforesources.com

National Minority Supplier Development Council (NMSDC)

1359 Broadway, 10th Floor
New York, NY 10018
(212) 944-2430
Fax (212) 719-9611
www.nmsdc.org

National Minority Supplier Development Council's primary objective is to provide a direct link between corporate America and minority-owned businesses. It was chartered in 1972 to provide increased procurement and business opportunities for minority businesses of all sizes.

The NMSDC network includes a National Office in New York and 39 regional councils across the country. The regional councils certify and match more than 15, 000 minority-owned businesses with member corporations that want to purchase goods and services.

Programs and Services:

- Certification of minority business enterprises (see Section 12 for more information on certification).
- Working capital loans to certified minority businesses which have contracts with NMSDC national and regional corporate members, through the Business Consortium Fund, as well as longer-term financing through the BCF's Specialized Small Business Investment Company (SSBIC).
- Educational seminars, training and technical assistance for buyers and suppliers to assist in personal and professional growth.
- Advanced Management Education Program, customized executive education, with highly intensive training and technical assistance for CEOs of minority-owned firms.
- Corporate Plus, a membership program for minority businesses with capability for national contracts.
- Business Opportunity Fairs which allow minority entrepreneurs to present themselves to hundreds of prospective buyers in a short time.
- NMSDC Annual Conference, the nations benchmark forum for minority business development.

US Pan Asian American Chamber of Commerce (USPAACC)

1329 18th Street, NW
Washington, DC 20036
202.296.5221
Fax 202.296.5225
www.uspaacc.com
membership@uspaacc.com

The US Pan Asian American Chamber of Commerce (USPAACC) was founded in 1984 as a national, non-profit business organization representing all Asian Americans and Asian American-related groups in business, sciences, the arts, sports, education, public and community services. USPAACC represents more than one ethnic group.

Our members' heritage includes China, Hong Kong, Taiwan, Japan, the Philippines, Korea, India, Vietnam, Cambodia, Thailand, Singapore, Malaysia, Pakistan, Mongolia and Indonesia.

MISSION: We promote, nurture and propel economic growth by opening doors of contract, education and professional opportunities for Asian Americans and their business partners in corporate America and government agencies.

US Hispanic Chamber of Commerce

1424 K Street NW Suite 401
Washington, DC 20005
800-USHCC86; 202- 842-1212
Fax: 202-842-3221
www.ushcc.com

In 1979, several dedicated Hispanic leaders realized the enormous potential of the Hispanic business community in the United States and envisioned the need for a national organization to represent its interests before the public and private sectors. Later that year, the United States Hispanic Chamber of Commerce (USHCC) was incorporated in the state of New Mexico, creating a structured organization aimed at developing a business network that would provide the Hispanic community with cohesion and strength. Since its inception, the USHCC has worked towards bringing the issues and concerns of the nation's more than 2 million Hispanic-owned businesses to the forefront of the national economic agenda. Throughout its nearly 25-year history, the Chamber has enjoyed outstanding working relationships with international Heads of State, Members of Congress and the current White House Administration. Through its network of more than 150 local Hispanic Chambers of Commerce and Hispanic business organizations, the USHCC effectively communicates the needs and potential of Hispanic enterprise to the public and private sector in several ways including:

- Implementing and strengthening national programs that assist the economic development of Hispanic firms;
- Increasing business relationships and partnerships between the corporate sector and Hispanic-owned businesses;
- Promoting international trade between Hispanic businesses in the United States and Latin America;
- Monitoring legislation, policies and programs that affect the Hispanic business community;
- and Providing technical assistance to Hispanic business associations and entrepreneurs.

MISSION: To advocate, promote and facilitate the success of Hispanic businesses

REGIONAL MINORITY SUPPLIER DEVELOPMENT COUNCILS

Affiliated with the National Minority Supplier Development Council, the regional councils enhance economic development opportunities for minority businesses through their programs and activities.

ALABAMA

South Regions Minority Business Council - SRMBC
Alex Alvarez, President and CEO
4715 Alton Ct
Birmingham, AL 35210
(205) 957-1883
Fax (205) 957-2114
www.srmbc.org
info@srmbc.org

ARIZONA

Grand Canyon Minority Supplier Development Council - GCMSDC
Ron Williams, President/CEO
340 East Palm Ln, Suite A-100
Phoenix, AZ 85004
(602) 495-9950
Fax (602) 495-9943
www.gcmsdc.org
grandcanyoncouncil@gcmsdc.org

ARKANSAS

Arkansas Mississippi Supplier Development Council, Inc - AMMSDC
Charles King, President/CEO
415 Main Street
Little Rock, AR 72201
(501) 374-7026
Fax (501) 371-0409
www.ammsdc.org
info@ammsdc.org

CALIFORNIA

Southern California Minority Business Development Council, Inc - SCMBDC
John W Murray, Jr, President
800 W 6th St, Ste 850
Los Angeles, CA 90017-2711
(213) 689-6960
Fax (213) 689-1707
www.scmbdc.org
info@scmbdc.org

Northern California Supplier Development Council - NCSDC
Scott Vowels, President
460 Hegenberger Road, Suite 730
Oakland, CA 94621
(510) 686-2555
Fax (510) 686-2552
www.ncsdc.org

San Diego Regional Minority Supplier Development Council
Ronald B Garnett, President/CEO
9903 BusinessPark Avenue suite 105
San Diego, CA 92131
(858) 537-2281
Fax (858) 537-2286
http://msdc.adaptone.com/gsdbdc
info@supplierdiversitysd.org

COLORADO

Rocky Mountain Minority Supplier Development Council - RMSDC
Stan Sena, President/CEO
1445 Market St, Ste 300
Denver, CO 80202
(303) 623-3037
Fax (303) 595-0027
www.rmmsdc.org
admin@rmmsdc.org

CONNECTICUT

Greater New England Minority Supplier Development Council - GNEMSDC
Dr Fred McKinney, President
4133 Whitney Ave, Building 4, Box 2
Hamden, CT 06518
(203) 288-9744
Fax (203) 288-9310
www.cmsdc.org

** As of January 1,2009 the New England Supplier Development Council (NEMSDC) and the Connecticut Minority Supplier Development Council (CMSDC) will be one council, representing all six New England States.**

FLORIDA

Florida Minority Supplier Development Council - FMSDC
Malik Ali, President
6880 Lake Ellenor Dr, Ste 104A
Orlando, FL 32809
(407) 245-6062
Fax (407) 857-8647
www.fmsdc.org

Southern Florida Minority Supplier Development Council
Beatrice Louissaint, President & CEO
9499 NE 2nd Ave #201
Miami, FL 33138
(305) 762-6151
Fax (305) 762-6158
www.sfmsdc.org
info@sfmsdc.org

GEORGIA

Georgia Minority Supplier Development Council - GMSDC
Stacey Key, President & CEO
58 Edgewood Avenue 5th Floor
Atlanta, GA 30303
(404) 589-4929
Fax (404) 589-4925
www.gmsdc.org
info@gmsdc.org

ILLINOIS

Chicago Minority Business Development Council, Inc - CMBDC
Sheila C. Hill, President
Clark Adams Building
105 W. Adams, Ste 2300
Chicago, IL 60601
(312) 755-8880
Fax (312) 755-8890
http://msdc.adaptone.com/cmbdc

INDIANA

Indiana Minority Supplier Development Council- IMSDC
Michelle Howell, President & CEO
2126 N Meridian St
Indianapolis, IN 46202
(317) 921-2680
Fax (317) 923-2204
www.imsdc.org

KENTUCKY

TriState Minority Supplier Development Council- TSMDC
Ty Gettis, President & CEO
614 W Main St, Ste 5500
Louisville, KY 40202
(502) 625-0159
Fax (502) 625-0082
www.tsmsdc.com
info@tsmsdc.com

LOUISIANA

Louisiana Minority Business Council – LAMBC
Phala K Mire, President /MBOC administrator
400 Poydras Street, Ste 1350
New Orleans, LA 70130
(504) 299-2960
Fax (504) 299-2961
www.lambc.org

MARYLAND

MD/DC Minority Supplier Development Council - MD/DCMSDC
Kenneth E Clark, President & CEO
Headquarters / Maryland Office
10770 Columbia Pike
Lower Level, Ste L100
Silver Spring, MD 20901
(301) 592-6700
Fax (301) 592-6704
www.mddccouncil.org

MASSACHUSETTS

As of January 1,2009 the New England Supplier Development Council (NEMSDC) and the Connecticut Minority Supplier Development Council (CMSDC) will be one council, representing all six New England States. Please refer to the Connecticut council for address and telephone information.

MICHIGAN

Michigan Minority Business Development Council - MMBDC
Louis Green, President/CEO
3011 W Grand Blvd, Ste 230
Detroit, MI 48202
(313) 873-3200
www.mmbdc.com

MINNESOTA

Midwest Minority Supplier Development Council - MMSDC
Steve Venable, President
111 3rd Avenue S., Ste 240
Minneapolis, MN 55401
(612) 465-8881
Fax (612) 465-8887
http://msdc.adaptone.com/mmsdc
info@mmsdc.org

MISSISSIPPI

Arkansas Mississippi Supplier Development Council, Inc - AMMSDC
Charles King, President/CEO
300 Spring Street, Ste 604
Little Rock, AR 72201
(501) 374-7026 or (877) 374-5677
Fax (501) 371-0409
www.ammsdc.org
info@ammsdc.org

MISSOURI

Mid-American Minority Business Development Council
Lonnie Scott, President
777 Admiral Boulevard
Kansas City, MO 64106
(816) 221-4200
Fax (816) 221-4212
http://msdc.sdaptone.com/mambdc/
info@mambdc.org

St Louis Minority Business Council - SLMBC
Jim Webb, President
308 North 21st St, Ste 700
St Louis, MO 63103
(314) 241-1143
Fax (314) 241-1073
www.slmbc.org
info@slmbc.org

NEBRASKA

Great Plains Minority Supplier Development Council, Inc - GPMSDC
Robert Morgan, President
9140 W Dodge Rd, Ste 225
Omaha NE, 68114
(402) 614-9355
Fax (402) 614-8824
www.gpmsdc.com

NEVADA

Nevada Minority Business Council - NVMBC
Dianne Fontes, President
1785 E Sahara Ave, Ste 360
Las Vegas, NV 89104
(702) 894-4477
www.nvmbc.org
nvminority@aol.com

NEW YORK

Upstate New York Regional Minority Purchasing Council, Inc - UNYRMPCI
Linda Terrell, President/CEO
85 River Rock Drive, Ste 113
Mail Stop 14
Buffalo, New York 14207
(716) 871-4120
Fax (716) 871-3725
www.unyrmpci.org
info@unyrpci.org

New York & New Jersey Minority Supplier Development Council - NYNJMSDC
Lynda Ireland, President & CEO
330 Seventh Avenue, 8th Fl
New York, NY 10001
(212) 502-5663
Fax (212) 502-5807
www.nynjmsdc.org
council@nynjmsdc.org

NORTH CAROLINA/ SOUTH CAROLINA

Carolinas Minority Supplier Development Council, Inc - CMSDC
Robin Hamilton- President & CEO
1000 Seaboard Street Ste B-14
Charlotte, NC 28262
(704) 549-1000
Fax (704) 549-1616
http://msdc.adaptone.com/carolinasmsdc
info@carolinasmsdc.org

OHIO

Northern Ohio Minority Business Council - NOMBC
Alexis Clark-Amison, President
737 Bolivar Rd, Ste 4500
Cleveland, OH 44115
(216) 363-6300
Fax (216) 363-0001
www.app.suppliergateway.com/nombc
info@nombconline.org

South Central Ohio Minority Business Council-SCOMBC
Cathy Mock, President
100 East Broad Street Ste 2460
Columbus, OH 45215
(614) 225-6959
Fax (614) 225-1851
www.scombc.org
info@scombc.org

OKLAHOMA
Oklahoma Minority Supplier Development Council - OMSDC
Debra Ponder-Nelson, President & CEO
The Pavilion Building
6701 N Broadway, Ste 216
Oklahoma City, OK 73116
(405) 767-9900
Fax (405) 767-9901
www.omsdc.org
oklamsdc@aol.com

PENNSYLVANIA
Western Pennsylvania Minority Supplier Development Council -WPMSDC
Alexander "Nick" Nichols Jr., President
Regional Enterprise Towers
425 Sixth Ave, Ste 2690
Pittsburgh, PA 15219
(412) 391-4423
Fax (412) 391-3132
www.prmpc.org

Minority Supplier Development Council of Pennsylvania, New Jersey and Delaware - MSDC of PA-NJ-DE
Darlene Jenkins, CEO
42 South 15th St, Ste 1400
Philadelphia, PA 19102
(215) 569-1005
Fax (215) 569-2667
http://msdc.adaptone.com/panjde
info@msdc-panjde.org

PUERTO RICO
Puerto Rico Minority Supplier Development Council, Inc - SDMSDC
Jaqueline Marie Matos, President
PO Box 192410
San Juan, PR 00919-2410
(787) 759-9445
www.prmsdc.org

TENNESSEE
Tennessee Minority Supplier Development Council - TMSDC
Cheri K. Henderson, President
Plaza One Building
220 Athens Way, Suite 105
Nashville, TN 37228
(615) 259-4699
www.tmsdc.net
info@tmsdc.net

TEXAS
Southwest Minority Supplier Development Council-- SMSDC
Dinah Lovett, President
912 Bastrop Hwy, Ste 101
Austin, TX 78741
Austin (512) 386-8766 Fax (512) 386-8988
http://smsdc.org/
admin@smsdc.org

Dallas / Fort Worth Minority Business Development Council - DFWMBDC
Margo J Posey, President and CEO
2710 N Stemmons Fwy
Stemmons Tower North, Suite 900
Dallas, TX 75207
(214) 630-0747
Fax (214) 637-2241
http://msdc.adaptone.com/dfwmbdc/
business@dfwmbdc.com

Houston Minority Business Council - HMBC
Richard A Huebner, President
3 Riverway Suite 555
Houston , TX 77056
(713) 271-7805
Fax (713) 271-9770
www.hmbc.org
info@hmbc.org

VIRGINIA
Virginia Minority Supplier Development Council - VMSDC
Tracey Jeter, President
9210 Arboretum Parkway, Ste 150
Richmond, VA 23236
(804) 320-2100
Fax (804) 320-3966
www.vmsdc.org

WASHINGTON

Northwest Minority Business Council - NMBC
Fernando Martinez, President & CEO
320 Andover Park E, Ste 205
Tukwila, WA 98188-7635
(206) 575-7748
Fax (206) 575-7783
http://msdc.adaptone.com/nwmsdc/
info@northwestmsdc.org

WISCONSIN

Wisconsin, Iowa, and Central Illinois Supplier Development Council
Floyd Rose, PhD, President
PO Box 8577
Madison, WI 53708-8577
(608) 241-5858
Fax (608) 241-9100
www.suppliercouncil.org
councilenterprises@sbcglobal.net

OTHER PRIVATE SECTOR RESOURCES

American Business Women's Association (ABWA)
9100 Ward Parkway
PO Box 8728
Kansas City, MO 64114-0728
(800) 228-0007
Fax (816) 361-4991
www.abwa.org

Americans for Indian Opportunities
1001 Marquette Ave
Albuquerque, NM 87102
(505) 842-8677
Fax (505) 842-8658
www.aio.org
aio@aio.org

Asian American Alliance
1 International Blvd Ste 203
Mahwah, NJ 07495
(201) 252-8252
www.asianamericanalliance.com
info@asianamericanalliance.com

Asian Business Association
120 San Pedro Street Ste 523
Los Angeles, CA 90012
(213) 628-1222
Fax (213) 628-3222
www.aba-la.org
info@aba-la.org

Asian Chamber of Commerce
7217 North 6th Way
Phoenix, AZ 85020
(602) 222-2009
Fax (602) 870-7562
www.asianchamber.org

Asian Pacific American Women's Leadership Institute
1820 14th Street Ste 500
Santa Monica, CA 90404
Fax (925) 605-3614
www.apawli.org
apawli@rabriam.com

Association of American Indian Affairs
966 Hungerford Dr, Ste 12-B
Rockville, MD 20850
(240) 314-7155
Fax (240) 314-7159
www.indian-affairs.org
general.aaia@verizon.net

Association of African American Women Business Owners (AAWBOA)
3363 Alden Place NE
Washington D.C. 20019
(202) 399-3645
aawboa@aol.com

BidNet
20A Railroad Ave
Albany, NY 12205-0600
(800) 677-1997
www.bidnet.com
info@bidnet.com

Black Women's Forum
3870 Crenshaw Blvd
Los Angeles, CA 90008
(323) 292-3009

Catalyst
120 Wall Street, 5th Fl
New York, NY 10005
(212) 514-7600
Fax (212) 514-8470
www.catalyst.org
info@catalyst.org

Congressional Black Caucus Foundation Inc.
1720 Massachusetts Avenue NW
Washington, DC 20036
(202) 263-2800
Fax (202) 775-0773
www.cbcfinc.org
info@cbcfinc.org

The Institute for Supply Management (ISM)
(Formerly NAPM)
PO Box 22160
Tempe, AZ 85285-2160
(800) 888-6276 or (480) 752-6276
Fax (480) 752-7890
www.ism.ws

International Franchise Association (IFA)
1501 K St NW, Ste 350
Washington, DC 20005
(202) 628-8000
Fax (202) 628-0812
www.franchise.org

Latin Business Association
120 S San Pedro St, Ste 530
Los Angeles, CA 90012
(213) 628-8510
Fax(213) 628-8519
www.lbausa.com

Latin American Management Association
419 New Jersey Ave SE
Washington, DC 20003
(202) 546-3803 or (888) 526-2932
Fax (202) 546-3807
www.buscapique.com/latinusa/buscafile/wash/lama.htm

Minority Business Enterprise Legal Defense and Education Fund, Inc
1100 Mercantile Ln, Ste 115-A
Largo, MD 20774
(301) 583-4648
Fax (301) 772-8392
www.mbeldef.org

National Association for the Advancement of Colored People (NAACP)
4805 Mt Hope Dr
Baltimore, MD 21215
(410) 580-5777 or (877) 622-2798
www.naacp.org

National Association of Investment Companies (NAIC)
1300 Pennsylvania Ave NW, Ste 700
Washington, DC 20004
(202) 204-3001
Fax (202) 204-3022
www.naicvc.com
inquires@naicvc.com

National Association of Minority Contractors
2307 Skyland Place SE, Ste A
Washington, DC 20020
(202) 678-8840
Fax (202) 678-8842
www.namcdc.net
info@namcdc.org

National Association of Negro Business & Professional Women's Clubs, Inc
1806 New Hampshire Ave NW
Washington, DC 20009
(202) 483-4206
www.nanbpwc.org
info@nanbpwc.org

National Black Chamber of Commerce
1350 Connecticut Ave NW, Ste 405
Washington, DC 20036
(202) 466-6888
Fax (202) 466-4918
www.nationalbcc.org
info@nationalbcc.org

National Black MBA Association (NBMBAA)
180 N Michigan Ave Ste. 1400
Chicago, IL 60601
(312) 236-2622
Fax (312) 236-0390
www.nbmbaa.org
mail@nbmbaa.org

National Center for American Indian Enterprise Development (NCAIED)
953 E Juanita Ave
Mesa, AZ 85204
(480) 545-1298
Fax (480) 545-4208
www.ncaied.org

National Council of LaRaza
1126 16th St NW
Raul Yzaguirre Building
Washington, DC 20036
(202) 785-1670
Fax (202) 776-1793
www.nclr.org
comments@nclr.org

National Hispanic Corporate Council
1555 Wilson Boulevard, Ste 510
Arlington, VA 22209
(703) 807-5137
Fax (703) 842-7924
www.nhcchq.org

National Minority Business Council
120 Broadway 19th floor
New York, NY 10271
(212) 693-5050 or (866) 523-NMBC
Fax (212) 693-5048
www.nmbc.org
nmbc@msn.com

National Urban League
120 Wall St
New York, NY 10005
(212) 558-5300
Fax (212) 344-5332
www.nul.org
info@nul.org

Opportunities Industrialization Centers of America, Inc.
1415 N Broad St, Ste 227
Philadelphia, PA 19122-3323
(215) 236-4500
Fax (215) 236-7480
www.oicofamerica.org
info@oicofamerica.org

Rainbow/PUSH Coalition
930 E 50th St
Chicago, IL 60615-2702
(773) 373-3366
Fax (773) 373-3571
www.rainbowpush.org
info@rainbowpush.org

US Chamber of Commerce
1615 H St NW
Washington, DC 20062-2000
(202) 659-6000 or (800) 638-6582
www.uschamber.com

SECTION 15

HISTORICALLY BLACK COLLEGES AND UNIVERSITIES (HBCUs)

www.hbcu-central.com

HJBCUs were "invented" in 1837, 26 years before the end of slavery. Richard Humphreys, a Quaker philanthropist, founded the Institute for Colored Youth to train free blacks to become teachers.

Over 100 years later, Historically Black Colleges and Universities stills stand. Their character and missions will continue to change and evolve but best believe they will be around for many years to come.

ALABAMA

Alabama A&M University
Huntsville, AL 35811
(256) 372-5000
www.aamu.edu

Alabama State University
Montgomery, AL 36101
(334) 229-4984
www.alasu.edu

Bishop State Community College
Mobile, AL 36603
(251) 405-7000
www.bscc.cc.al.us

Concordia College
Selma, AL 36701
(334) 874-5700
www.concordiaselma.edu

Gadsen State Community College
Gadsen, AL 35902
(256) 549-8672
www.gadsenstate.edu

JF Drake State Technical College
Huntsville, AL 35811
(256) 539-8161
www.dstc.cc.al.us

Lawson State Community College
Birmingham, AL 35221
(205) 929-6309
www.ls.cc.al.us

Miles College
Fairfield, AL 35064
(205) 929-1000
www.miles.edu

Oakwood College
Huntsville, AL 35896
(256) 716-7000
www.oakwood.edu

Selma University
Selma, AL 36701
(334) 872-2533 x18
http://selmauniversity.org

Shelton State Community College
Tuscaloosa, AL 35405
(205) 391-2214
www.shelton.cc.al.us

Stillman College
Tuscaloosa, AL 35403
(800) 841-5722
www.stillman.edu

Talladega College
Talladega, AL 35160
(256) 761-6235
www.talladega.edu

Trenholm State Technical College
Montgomery, AL 36108
(334) 832-9000
www.trenholmtech.cc.al.us

Tuskegee University
Tuskegee, AL 36088
(334) 727-8011
www.tuskegee.edu

ARKANSAS

Arkansas Baptist College
Little Rock, AR 72202-6099
(501) 374-7856
www.arbaptcol.edu

Philander Smith College
Little Rock, AR 72202
(501) 370-5221
www.philander.edu

Shorter College
North Little Rock, AR 72114
(501) 374-6305
www.shorterjrcollege.com

University of Arkansas at Pine Bluff
Pine Bluff, AR 71601
(870) 575-8492
www.uapb.edu

CALIFORNIA

Charles Drew University Of Medicine and Science
Los Angeles, CA 90059
(323) 563-4839
www.cdrewu.edu

DELAWARE

Delaware State University
Dover, DE 19901
(302) 857-6060
www.desu.edu

DISTRICT OF COLUMBIA

Howard University
Washington, DC 20059
(202) 806-6100
www.howard.edu

University of the District of Columbia
Washington, DC 20008
(202) 274-5000
www.udc.edu

FLORIDA

Bethune-Cookman University
Daytona Beach, FL 32114
(386) 481-2000
www.cookman.edu

Edward Waters College
Jacksonville, FL 32209
(904) 355-3030
www.ewc.edu

Florida A&M University
Tallahassee, FL 32307
(850) 599-3000
www.famu.edu

Florida Memorial College
Miami, FL 33054
(305) 625-3600
www.fmc.edu

GEORGIA

Albany State University
Albany, GA 31705
(229) 430-4646
www.asurams.edu

Clark Atlanta University
Atlanta, GA 30314
(800) 688-3228
www.cau.edu

Fort Valley State University
Fort Valley, GA 31030
(478) 825-6280
www.fvsu.edu

Interdenominational Theological Center
Atlanta, GA 30314
(404) 527-7792
www.itc.edu

Morehouse College
Atlanta, GA 30314
(404) 681-2800
www.morehouse.edu

Morehouse School of Medicine
Atlanta, GA 30310
(404) 752-1500
www.msm.edu

Morris Brown College
Atlanta, GA 30314
(404) 739-1000
www.morrisbrown.edu

Paine College
Augusta, GA 30901-3182
(706) 821-8200
www.paine.edu

Savannah State University
Savannah, GA 31404
(912) 356-2181
www.savstate.edu

Spelman College
Atlanta, GA 30314
(404) 681-3643
www.spelman.edu

ILLINOIS

Chicago State University
Chicago, IL 60628
(773) 995-2513
www.csu.edu

KENTUCKY

Kentucky State University
Frankfort, KY 40601
(502) 597-6000
www.kysu.edu

Simmons College of Kentucky
Louisville, KY 40210
(502) 776-1443
www.simmonscollegeky.edu

LOUISIANA

Dillard University
New Orleans, LA 70122
(504) 283-8822
www.dillard.edu

Grambling State University
Grambling, LA 71245
(800) 569-4714
www.gram.edu

Southern University and A&M College
Baton Rouge, LA 70813
(225) 771-4500
www.subr.edu

Xavier University of Louisiana
New Orleans, LA 70125-1098
(504) 486-7411
www.xula.edu

MARYLAND

Bowie State University
Bowie, MD 20715
(301) 860-4000
www.bowiestate.edu

Coppin State College
Baltimore, MD 21216
(410) 951-3600
www.coppin.edu

Morgan State University
Baltimore, MD 21251
(443) 885-3185
www.morgan.edu

University of Maryland Eastern Shore
Princess Anne, MD 21853
(410) 651-2200
www.umes.edu

MICHIGAN

Lewis College of Business
Detroit, MI 48235
(313) 862-6300
www.lewiscollege.edu

MISSISSIPPI

Alcorn State University
Alcorn State, MS 39096
(601) 877-6100
www.alcorn.edu

Coahoma Community College
Clarksdale, MS 38614-9799
(662) 627-2571
www.ccc.cc.ms.us

Hinds Community College
Raymond, MS 39154-1100
(601) 857-5261
www.hindscc.edu

Jackson State University
Jackson, MS 39217
(800) 848-6817
www.jsums.edu

Mary Holmes College
West Point, MS 39773
(662) 495-5100
www.maryholmes.edu

Mississippi Valley State University
Itta Bena, MS 38941-1400
(662) 254-3347
www.mvsu.edu

Rust College
Holly Springs, MS 38635-2328
(601) 252-8000 ext 4059
www.rustcollege.edu

Tougaloo College
Tougaloo, MS 39174
(601) 977-7700
www.tougaloo.edu

MISSOURI

Harris-Stowe State University
St Louis, MO 63103
(314) 340-3300
www.hssu.edu

Lincoln University-Missouri
Jefferson City, MO 65102
(314) 681-5000
www.lincolnu.edu

NEW YORK

CUNY - The Medgar Evers College
Brooklyn, NY 11225
(718) 270-6024
www.mec.cuny.edu

NORTH CAROLINA

Barber-Scotia College
Concord, NC 28025
(704) 789-2900
www.b-sc.edu

Bennett College
Greensboro, NC 27401-3239
(800) 413-5323
www.bennett.edu

Elizabeth City State University
Elizabeth City, NC 27909
(225) 335-3400
www.ecsu.edu

Fayetteville State University
Fayetteville, NC 28301-4298
(910) 672-1111
www.uncfsu.edu

Johnson C Smith University
Charlotte, NC 28216
(704) 378-1000
www.jcsu.edu

Livingstone College
Salisbury, NC 28144
(800) 835-3435
www.livingstone.edu

North Carolina A&T State University
Greensboro, NC 27411
(800) 443-8964
www.ncat.edu

North Carolina Central University
Durham, NC 27707
(919) 560-6100
www.nccu.edu

Saint Augustines College
Raleigh, NC 27610
(919) 516-4000
www.st-aug.edu

Shaw University
Raleigh, NC 27601
(919) 546-8650
www.shawuniversity.edu

Winston-Salem State University
Winston-Salem, NC 27110
(336) 750-2000
www.wssu.edu

OHIO

Central State University
Wilberforce, OH 45384-3002
(937) 376-6011
www.centralstate.edu

Wilberforce University
Wilberforce, OH 45384-3001
(937) 708-5721
www.wilberforce.edu

OKLAHOMA

Langston University
Langston, OK 73050
(405) 466-2231
www.lunet.edu

PENNSYLVANIA

Cheyney University of PA
Cheyney, PA 19319-0019
(610) 399-2000
www.cheyney.edu

Lincoln University-Pennsylvania
Lincoln University, PA 19352
(610) 932-1209
www.lincoln.edu

SOUTH CAROLINA

Allen University
Columbia, SC 29204
(803) 376-5700
www.allenuniversity.edu

Benedict College
Columbia, SC 29204
(803) 253-5143
www.benedict.edu

Claflin University
Orangeburg, SC 29115
(803) 535-5000
www.claflin.edu

Clinton Junior College
Rock Hill, SC 29730
(803) 327-7402
www.clintonjuniorcollege.edu

Denmark Technical College
Denmark, SC 29042
(803) 793-5176
www.denmarktech.edu

Morris College
Sumter, SC 29150
(803) 934-3200
www.morris.edu

South Carolina State University
Orangeburg, SC 29117
(803) 536-7000
www.scsu.edu

Voorhees College
Denmark, SC 29042
(803) 793-3351
www.voorhees.edu

TENNESSEE

Fisk University
Nashville, TN 37208
(615) 329-8500
www.fisk.edu

Knoxville College
Knoxville, TN 37921
(865) 524-6603
www.knoxvillecollege.edu

Lane College
Jackson, TN 38301
(731) 426-7500
www.lanecollege.edu

Lemoyne-Owen College
Memphis, TN 38126
(901) 435-1000
www.loc.edu

Meharry Medical College
Nashville, TN 37208-3599
(615) 327-6111
www.mmc.edu

Tennessee State University
Nashville, TN 37209-1561
(615) 963-5101
www.tnstate.edu

TEXAS

Huston-Tillotson College
Austin, TX 78702-2795
(512) 505-3000
www.htu.edu

Jarvis Christian College
Hawkins, TX 75765
(903) 769-5700
www.jarvis.edu

Paul Quinn College
Dallas, TX 75241
(214) 376-1000
www.pqc.edu

Prairie View A&M University
Prairie View, TX 77446-3089
(936) 857-3311
www.pvamu.edu

Southwestern Christian College
Terrell, TX 75160
(972) 524-3341
www.swcc.edu

St. Phillips College
San Antonio, TX 78203
(201) 531-3200
www.accd.edu/spc

Texas College
Tyler, TX 75712
(903) 593-8311
www.texascollege.edu

Texas Southern University
Houston, TX 77004-9987
(713) 313-7071
www.tsu.edu

University of Texas at El Paso
El Paso, TX 79968
(915) 747-5890
www.utep.edu

Wiley College
Marshall, TX 75670
(903) 927-3300
www.wileyc.edu

US VIRGIN ISLANDS

University of the Virgin Islands
St Thomas, VI 00802-9990
(340) 776-9200
www.uvi.edu

VIRGINIA

Hampton University
Hampton, VA 23668
(757) 727-5000
www.hamptonu.edu

Norfolk State University
Norfolk, VA 23504-8026
(757) 238-6000
www.nsu.edu

Saint Paul's College
Lawrenceville, VA 23868
(434) 848-6431
www.saintpauls.edu

Virginia State University
Petersburg, VA 23806
(804) 524-5902
www.vsu.edu

Virginia Union University
Richmond, VA 23220
(804) 257-5600
www.vuu.edu

Virginia University of Lynchburg
Lynchburg, VA 24501-6417
(434) 528-5276
www.vuonline.org

WEST VIRGINIA

Bluefield State College
Bluefield, WV 24701-2198
(304) 327-4000
www.bluefieldstate.edu

West Virginia State University
Institute, WV 25112-1000
(800) 987-2112
www.wvsc.edu

SECTION 16

DIVERSE SUPPLIER DIRECTORIES & DATABASES

ALASKA

Department of Transportation & Public Facilities
Office of Commissioner
3132 Channel Dr
Juneau, AK 99811-2500
(907) 465-3900
http://www.dot.state.ak.us/

Municipality of Anchorage
Office of Equal Opportunity
632 W 6th Ave, Ste 620
Anchorage, AK 99501
(907) 343-4878
www.muni.org/oeo/dwbe.cfm

ARIZONA

Grand Canyon Minority Supplier Development Council
340 East Palm Lane Ste. A-100
Phoenix, AZ 85004
(602) 495-9950
Fax (602) 495-9943
www.gcmsdc.org

National Center for American Indian Enterprise Development
National Center Headquarters
953 E Juanita Ave
Mesa, AZ 85204
(480) 545-1298
Fax (480) 545-4208
www.ncaied.org/

ARKANSAS

Arkansas State Highway & Transportation Department
Program & Contract Division
PO Box 2261
10324 Interstate 30
Little Rock, AR 72203-2261
(501) 569-2000
Fax (501) 569-2400
www.arkansashighways.com
info@arkansashighways.com

Arkansas Economic Development Commission
One Capitol Mall
Little Rock, AR 72201
(501) 682-1121or (800) ARKANSAS
Fax (501) 682-7394
www.arkansasedc.com
info@arkansasedc.com

CALIFORNIA

Department of Transportation
Civil Rights Program - MS #79
1823 14th Street
Sacramento, CA 95814
(916) 324-1700 or (866) 810-6346
Fax (916) 324-1949
www.dot.ca.gov/hq/bep/

Hispanic Business
425 Pine Ave
Santa Barbara, CA 93117
(805) 964-4554
Fax (805) 964-5539
www.hispanicbusiness.com/

Hispanic Chamber of Commerce, Santa Barbara
PO Box 6592
Santa Barbara, CA 93160-6592
(805) 637-3680
Fax (805) 681-1260
www.sbhispanicchamber.org

Hispanic Chamber of Commerce, Silicon Valley
310 South First Street
San Jose, CA 95113
(408) 213-0320
Fax (408) 282-7071
www.hccsv.org
info@hccsv.org

Human Rights Commission of San Francisco
25 Van Ness Ave, Ste 800
San Francisco, CA 94102-6033
(415) 252-2500
Fax (415) 431-5764
www.sfgov.org/site/sfhumanrights_index.asp
hrc.info@sfgov.gov

Office of Affirmative Action Compliance, LA County
780 Kenneth Hahn Hall of Administration
500 W Temple St, Ste 780, 7th floor
Los Angeles, CA 90012
(213) 974-1080
http://oaac.co.la.ca.us

CONNECTICUT

Greater New England Minority Supplier Development Council - GNEMSDC
Dr Fred McKinney, President
4133 Whitney Ave, Building 4, Box 2
Hamden, CT 06518
(888) 874-7114 or (203) 288-9744
Fax (203) 288-9310

** As of January 1,2009 the New England Supplier Development Council (NEMSDC) and the Connecticut Minority Supplier Development Council (CMSDC) will be one council, representing all six New England States.**

DELAWARE

Economic Development Office (DEDO
City of Dover
99 Kings Highway
Dover, DE 19901
(302) 739-4271
Fax (302) 739-5749
www.dedo.deleware.gov

DISTRICT OF COLUMBIA

American Council of Engineering Companies
Research Management Foundation
1015 15th St NW, 8th Fl
Washington, DC 20005-2605
(202) 347-7474
Fax (202) 898-0068
www.acec.org
acec@acec.org

US Hispanic Chamber of Commerce
2175 K St NW, Ste 100
Washington, DC 20037
(202) 842-1212
Fax (202) 842-3221
www.ushcc.com

FLORIDA

Office of Supplier Diversity
Department of Management Services
4050 Esplanade Way
Tallahassee, FL 32399-0950
(850) 487-0915
Fax (850) 922-6852
www.dms.myflorida.com

Florida Regional Minority Business Council
9949 Northeast 2nd Avenue #201
Miami, FL 33138
(305) 762-6151
Fax (305) 762-6158
www.frmbc.org
frmbc@frmbc.org

Miami-Dade County
Department of Small Business Development
111 NW 1st St, 19th Fl
Miami, FL 33128-1900
(305) 375-3111
Fax (305) 375-3160
www.miamidade.gov

NMSDC of Florida
6880 Lake Ellenor Dr, Ste 104A
Orlando, FL 32809
(407) 245-6062
Fax (407) 857-8647
www.fmsdc.org
info@fmsdc.org

Orange County Business Development Dept
Purchasing and Contracts
400 E South St, IOC 11, 2nd floor
Orlando, FL 32801
(407) 836-5635
www.orangecountyfl.net/cms/dept/countyadmin/purcon/default

GEORGIA

BlackBusinessList.Com, LLC
P O Box 105603
Atlanta, GA 30348
(866) 681-9497
www.blackbusinesslist.com

MARTA- Headquarters
Department of Diversity & Equal Opportunity
2424 Piedmont Rd NE
Atlanta, GA 30324-3311
(404) 848-5000
www.itsmarta.com/

UIDA Business Services
86 S Cobb Dr, MZ0510
Marietta, GA 30063
(770) 494-0431
Fax (770) 494-1236
www.uida.org

HAWAII

State of Hawaii Dept. of Transportation
Office of Civil Rights
869 Punchbowl St, #112
Honolulu, HI 96813
(808) 587-5339
Fax (808) 587-2025
www.state.hi.us/dot/

ILLINOIS

City of Chicago - Procurement Department
121 N LaSalle St, Rm 800
Chicago, IL 60602
(312) 744-6249
Fax (312) 744-0246
www.cityofchicago.org

Illinois Department of Transportation
Bureau of Small Business Enterprise
2300 S Dirksen Pkwy
Springfield, IL 62764
(217) 782-7820
www.dot.state.il.us/

INDIANA

Minority and Women's Business Enterprises Division
402 W Washington St, Rm W469
Indianapolis, IN 46204
(317) 232-3061
mwbe@idoa.in.gov
www.in.gov/idoa/2867.htm

IOWA

Iowa Department of Transportation
Office of Contracts
800 Lincoln Way
Ames, IA 50010
(515) 239-1101
Fax (515) 239-1639
www.dot.state.ia.us/

KANSAS

Kansas Department of Commerce
1000 SW Jackson St, Ste 100
Topeka, Kansas 66612-1354
(785) 296-3481
Fax (785) 296-5055
www.kansascommerce.com

Kansas Department of Transportation
700 SW Harrison St
Topeka, KS 66603-3754
(785) 296-3566
Fax (785) 296-0287
www.ksdot.org
publicinfo@ksdot.org

KENTUCKY

Sustainable Urban Neighborhoods
SUN Program
University of Louisville
426 West Bloom St
Louisville, KY 40208
(502)852-8557
Fax (502) 852-4558
www.louisville.edu/org/sun/minority/

Kentucky Transportation Cabinet
200 Mero St
Frankfort, KY 40622
(502) 564-4890
www.transportation.ky.gov

LOUISIANA

Louisiana Economic Development
Small and Emerging Business Development
1051 N Third Street
Baton Rouge, LA 70804
(225) 342-4320 or (800) 450-8115
www.louisianaforward.com

MARYLAND

Governor's Office of Minority Affairs
6 St Paul Street, Ste 1502
Baltimore, MD 21202
(410) 767-8232
www.mdminoritybusiness.com
info@oma.state.md.us

Maryland Department of Transportation
Minority Business Enterprise
7201 Corporate Center Dr #548
Handover, MD 21076
(410) 865-1269 or (800)544-6056
www.mdot.state.md.us/MBE_Program/overview

MASSACHUSETTS

New England Minority Supplier Development Council -NEMSDC is now a part of the Greater New England Minority Supplier Development Council - GNEMSDC. Please refer to the Connecticut council for address and telephone information.

MINNESOTA

Minnesota Department of Transportation
Office of Civil Rights
395 John Ireland Blvd
St Paul, MN 55155
(800) 657-3774
www.dot.state.mn.us/civilrights/

Diversity Information Resources, Inc
2105 Central Avenue NE
Minneapolis, MN 55418-3767
(612) 781-6819
www.diversityinforesources.com

MISSISSIPPI

Mississippi Department of Transportation
Civil Rights Department
401 North West St
Jackson, MS 39201
(601) 359-7466
Fax (601) 359-7050
www.gomdot.com

Mississippi Development Authority
Minority Business Enterprise Division
501 North West Street
Jackson, MS 39201
(601) 359-3449
Fax (601) 359-2832
www.mississippi.org
minority@mississippi.org

MISSOURI

Kansas City Black Pages
1601 E 18th St, Ste 315
Kansas City, MO 64108
(816) 421-0400
Fax (816) 472-0240
www.duboislc.org/BlackPages/BlackPages.html

Missouri Department of Transportation
105 W Capitol
Jefferson City, MO 65102
(888) 275-6636
www.modot.org/business/

St Louis Black Pages
333 N Beaumont St
St Louis, MO 63103
(314) 531-7300
Fax (314) 531-7302
www.black-pages.com
info@black-pages.com

Office of Supplier And Workforce Diversity
State of Missouri
301 West High Street room 630
Jefferson City, MO 65101
(573) 751-8130 or (877) 259-2963
www.oswd.mo.gov

MONTANA

Montana Department of Transportation
Civil Rights Bureau --- DBE Program
2701 Prospect Ave
PO Box 201001
Helena, MT 59620-1001
(406) 444-6201
Fax (406) 444-7685
www.mdt.state.mt.us

NEVADA

Las Vegas Latin Chamber of Commerce
300 N 13th St
Las Vegas, NV 89101
(702) 385-7367
Fax (702) 385-2614
www.lvlcc.com

NEW JERSEY

New Jersey Dept of Transportation
Office of Civil Rights/Contract Compliance
PO Box 600
Trenton, NJ 08625-0600
(609) 292-6500
www.nj.gov/transportation/

NEW YORK

Black Enterprise Magazine Headquarters
Earl G Graves Publishing Co
130 Fifth Ave, 10th Fl
New York, NY 10011-4399
(212) 242-8000
www.blackenterprise.com

National Minority Business Council
120 Broadway 19th floor
New York, NY 10271
(212) 693-5050
Fax (212) 693-5048
www.nmbc.org

New York State Dept. of Economic Development
30 S Pearl St
Albany, NY 12245
(800) 782-8369
www.empire.state.ny.us
esd@empire.state.ny.us

NORTH CAROLINA

Carolinas Minority Supplier Development Council
10400 Mallard Creek Rd, Ste 206
Charlotte, NC 28262
(704) 549-1000
Fax (704) 549-1616
www.msdc.adaptone.com/carolinasmsdc

NC Department of Administration
Division Purchase/Contracts
116 West Jones Street 4th floor
Raleigh, NC 27603
(919) 807-4500
www.doa.state.nc.us/PandC/

NORTH DAKOTA

North Dakota Department of Transportation
Civil Rights
608 E Blvd Ave
Bismarck, ND 58505-0700
(701) 328-2637
www.dot.nd.gov
dot@nd.us

OHIO

City of Cleveland
Office of Economic Development
601 Lakeside Ave, Rm 210
Cleveland, OH 44114
(216) 664-2406
Fax (216) 664-3681
www.city.cleveland.oh.us

OKLAHOMA

Human Rights Commission
City of Tulsa
200 Civic Center
Tulsa, OK 74103
(918) 596-7818
www.cityoftulsa.org

OREGON

Office of Minority, Women & Emerging Small Business
Department of Consumer & Business Services
775 Summer Street NE, Ste 200
PO Box 14480
Salem, OR 97309-0405
(503) 986-0075
Fax (503) 373-7041
www.oregon.gov/dcbs/omwesb/

PENNSYLVANIA

Allegheny County
Office of Minority, Women and Disadvanted Business Enterprises
542 Forbes Ave, Rm 204
Pittsburgh, PA 15219
(412) 350-4309
Fax (412) 350-4915
www.county.allegheny.pa.us/mwdbe/
mwdbe@county.allegheny.pa.us

Philadelphia Office of Economic Opportunity
formerly the Minority Business Enterprise Council
1401 JFK Blvd, Ste 330
Philadelphia, PA 19102-1666
(215) 686-6232
www.phila.gov/mbec/

Pennsylvania Department of Transportation
Disadvantaged Business Enterprise Division
Bureau of Equal Opportunity
P.O. Box 3251
Harrisburg, PA 17105
(717) 787-5891
Fax (717) 717-4026
www.dot.state.pa.us

SOUTH CAROLINA

Columbia Midlands Black Pages
1913 Marion St, Ste 202
Columbia, SC 29201
(803) 254-6404 or (800) 419-2417
Fax (803) 254-6557
www.smallbusinesses.com/columbiamidlands.htm

South Carolina Minority Business Directory
Government Office of Small & Minority Business Assistance
1205 Pendleton St, Ste 440-A
Columbia, SC 29201
(803) 734-0657
Fax (803) 734-2498
www.govoepp.state.sc.us/osmba/
mwoodson@oepp.sc.gov

SOUTH DAKOTA
South Dakota Department of Transportation
Civil Right Compliance Office
700 E Broadway Avenue
Pierre, SD 57501
(605) 773-3540
Fax (605) 773-3921
www.sddot.com/civilrights.asp
june.hansen@state.sd.us

TENNESSEE
Governor's Office of Diversity Business Enterprise
27th Fl, William R. Snodgrass TN Tower
312 8th Ave N
Nashville, TN 37243
(615) 253-4657
www.tennessee.gov/businessopp/
richard.vannorman@state.tn.us

Tennessee Department of Transportation
James K Polk Bldg
505 Deaderick St, Ste 700
Nashville, TN 37243-0349
(615) 741-2848
Fax (615) 741-2508
www.tdot.state.tn.us
tdot.comments@state.tn.us

TEXAS
Dallas/Fort Worth Black Pages
3606 Marvin D Love Fwy, Ste 130
Dallas, TX 75224
(214) 375-5200
Fax (214) 375-5223

Greater Houston Black Pages
2016 Main St, Ste 1711
Houston, TX 77002
(713) 942-9344

UTAH
Department of Transportation
Office of Civil Rights
4501 S 2700 W, MS 141200
Salt Lake City, UT 84114-1200
(801) 965-4100
www.dot.state.ut.us

State Office of Black Affairs
324 S State, Ste 500
Salt Lake City, UT 84111
(801) 538-8829
Fax (801) 538-8678
http://dced.utah.gov/blackaffairs/

VIRGINIA
Commonwealth of Virginia
Department of Minority Business\Enterprise
1111 East Main Street suite 300
Richmond, VA 23219-1150
(804) 786-5560
Fax (804) 786-9736
www.dmbe.state.va.us
dmbe@dmbe.state.va.us

WASHINGTON
Washington State Office of Minority/Minority & Women's Business Enterprise
406 S Water St
P.O. Box 41160
Olympia, WA 98504
(360) 753-9693
Fax (360) 586-7079
www.omwbe.wa.gov

National Center for American Indian Enterprise Development
3327 NE 125th St, Ste 101
Seattle, WA 98125
(206) 365-7738
Fax (206) 365-7764
www.nwnabec.org

WEST VIRGINIA
West Virginia Small Business Development Center
1900 Kanawna Blvd E, Rm 652 Bldg 6
Charleston, WV 25305-0311
(304) 558-2960 or (888) 982-7232
Fax (304) 558-0127
www.sbdcwv.org

SECTION 17

2010 CALENDAR OF EVENTS
TRADE SHOWS, SEMINARS/WORKSHOPS

Please see the Calendar at www.diversityinforesources.com for updates as they become available.

JANUARY 2010

January 13-15, 2010
Rainbow Push Coalition
2010 13th Annual Wall Street Project Conference
New York, NY
(212) 425-7874
www.rainbowpush.org

January 15-17, 2010
Franchise Expo South
Miami, FL
(201) 226-1130
www.franchiseexpo.com

January 21, 2010
Mid-American Minority Development Council
24th Annual Awards Luncheon
Overland Park, KS
(816) 221-4200
www.mambdc.org

FEBRUARY 2010

February 2-4, 2010
Institute for Supply Management
7th Annul Black Executive Supply Management Summit
San Diego, CA
(800) 888-6276 or (480) 752-6276 ext. 3061
www.ism.ws

February 5-8, 2010
International Franchise Association (IFA)
50th Annual International Franchise Convention
San Antonio, TX
(202) 662-0784
www.franchise.org

February 6, 2010
Harvard Business School's Women's Student Association
19th Annual Dynamic Women in Business Conference
Boston, MA
(617) 495-6155
www.hbswsa.org

February 10-13, 2010
Black Enterprise
5th Annual 2010 Women of Power Summit
La Quinta, CA
(212) 242-8000
www.blackenterprise.com

February 17-18, 2010
Diversity Information Resources (DIR) Supplier Diversity Seminar
"Building Strategic Phases of a Supplier Diversity Process"
Scottsdale, AZ
(612) 781-6819
www.diversityinforesources.com

February 17, 2010
Wisconsin Supplier Development Council
John Deere Supplier Diversity Symposium
Moline, IL
(608) 241-5858
www.suppliercouncil.org

February 21-24, 2010
National Center for American Indian Enterprise Development
24th Annual Reservation Economic Summit & American Indian Business Trade Fair- RES2010
Las Vegas, NV
(800) 462-2433 x243
www.ncaied.org

February 25, 2010
Puerto Rico Supplier Diversity Council
2010 Opportunity Fair
Dorado, PR
(787) 627-7268
www.sdcpr.org

February 25, 2010
Southern California Minority Business Developement Council
2010 Minority Business Opportunity Day (MBOD)
Pacific Palms Conference Resort
Industry, CA
(213) 689-6960
www.scmbdc.org

February 25, 2010
Pittsburgh Regional Minority Purchasing Council
Supplier Diversity Summit
Pittsburgh, PA
(412) 391-4423
www.prmpc.org

MARCH 2010

March 2, 2010
Business & Professional Women USA
Policy & Action Day 2010
Washington, DC
(202) 777-8920
www.bpwusa.org

March 5, 2010
Northwest Minority Supplier Development Council
2010 Summit Awards Gala
Seattle, WA
(206) 575-7748
www.nmbc.biz

March 7-13, 2010
National Association of Women in Construction
13th Annual Women in Construction Week
Las Vegas, NV
(817) 877-5551
www.nawic.org

March 9, 2010
Dallas Fort Worth Minority Business Development Council
Hard Hat Construction Expo
Dallas, TX
(214) 630-0747
www.dfwmbdc.com

March 11-12, 2010
Florida Regional Minority Business Council
25th Annual Business Expo
Fort Lauderdale, FL
(305) 762-6151
www.frmbc.org

March 12, 2010
Northern California Supplier Development Council
Excellence in Supplier Diversity Awards Gala
San Francisco, CA
(510) 686-2555
www.ncsdc.org

March 17-18, 2010
Enterprising Women Inc.
2010 Enterprising Women of the Year Awards
Miami, FL
(919) 362-1551
www.enterprisingwomen.com

March 19, 2010
NAWBO-LA
24th Annual Leadership Awards Luncheon
Beverly Hills, CA
(213) 622-3200
www.nawbola.org

March 21, 2010
National Association of Education Buyers
89th Annual Meeting & Exposition
Denver, CO
(443) 543-5540
www.naepnet.org

March 23-24, 2010
WBENC
2010 WBENC Summit and Salute to Women's Business Enterprises
National Harbor, MD
(919) 362-1551
www.enterprisingwomen.com

March 24, 2010
Latino Business Conexion
Orange County's Largest Mixer VI
Costa Mesa, CA
(949) 222-6600
www.largestmixer.com/ocmixer/

March 25, 2010
Georgia Minority Supplier Development Council
Business Opportunity Expo and Awards Gala
Atlanta, GA
(404) 589-4929
www.gmsdc.or

March 29, 2010
Chicago Minority Business Development Council
43rd Annual Chicago Business Opportunity Fair
Navy Pier
Chicago, IL
(312) 755-8880
www.cmbdc.org

March (TBD), 2010
Golden Triangle Minority Business Council
Global Procurement Summit
League City, TX
(409) 962-8530
www.gtmbc.com

March (TBD), 2010
Southwest Minority Supplier Development Council
Champions in Diversity
San Antonio, TX
(512) 386-8766
www.smsdc.org

APRIL 2010

April 1-2, 2010
Women's Business Council - Southwest
SW Women's BusinessWorks Trade Show
Frisco, TX
(817) 299-0566 ext 208
www.wbcsouthwest.org

April 9-11, 2010
International Franchise Association (IFA)
19th Annual International Franchise Expo
Washington, DC
(201) 226-1130 ext 202
www.ifeinfo.com

April 11-14, 2010
National Native American Purchasing Association
20th Annual NNAPA Conference
Chandler, AZ
(509) 458-6550
groups.msn.com/NNAPA

April 14-15, 2010
Indiana Business Diversity Council
Indiana Business Opportunity Fair
Indianapolis, IN
(317) 923-2110
www.inbdc.org

April 21, 2010
Federal Small Business Technology Council, Inc
20th Annual OSDBU Procurement Conference
Chantilly, VA
(800) 878-2940
www.fbcinc.com/osdbu/

April 22-23, 2010
Wisconsin Supplier Development Council
Partners for Profit Trade Fair
Green Bay, WI
(608) 241-5858
www.suppliercouncil.org

April 22-24, 2010
Women Presidents Organization
13th Annual Conference 2010
Fort Lauderdale, FL
(212) 688-4114
www.womenpresidentsorg.com

April 23-24, 2010
Connecticut Minority Supplier Development Council
34th Annual Award Banquet
Boston, MA
(203) 288-9744
www.cmsdc.org

April 25-27, 2010
Institute for Supply Management (ISM, formerly NAPM)
95th Annual International Supply Management Conference & Educational Exhibit
San Diego, CA
(800) 888-6276
www.ism.ws

April 27-29, 2010
DiversityBusiness.com
10th Annual National Multicultural Business Conference and Awards Ceremony
National Harbor, Washington D.C.
(203) 255-2972

April (TBD), 2010
Rockville Chamber of Commerce
9th Annual Women In Business Conference
Montgomery County, MD
(301) 424-9300 x106
www.women-in-business.org

April (TBD), 2010
National Association of Women Business Owners (NAWBO)
Women In Business Trade Mission
(800) 556-2926 ext 4555
national@nawbo.org
www.nawbo.org

April (TBD), 2010
Maryland/DC Minority Supplier Development Council
2010 Business Conference/Opportunity Fair
Ellicott City, MD
(301) 592-6700
www.mddccouncil.org

MAY 2010

May 2-7, 2010
Amos Tuck School of Business Administration
Dartmouth College
Advanced Minority Business Executive Program
(Building a High-Performance Minority Business)
Hanover, NH
(603) 646-3740
www.tuck.dartmouth.edu

May 3-4, 2010
Virginia Regional Minority Supplier Development Council
Virginia Business Opportunity Fair
Richmond, VA
(804) 320-2100
www.vmsdc.org

May 4, 20140
Women Leading Kentucky
11th Annual Business & Leadership Conference
Lexington, KY
(859) 269-3503
www.womenleadingky.com

May 4-6, 2010
Michigan Minority Business Development Council
29th Annual Michigan Procurement Conference & Trade Fair
Detroit, MI
(313) 873-3200 x107
www.mmbdc.com

May 7, 2010
Council Enterprises Inc.
State Farm Insurance Co. Supplier Diversity Symposium
Bloomington, IL
(608) 241-5858
www.suppliercouncil.org

May 16-19, 2010
Black Enterprise
15th Annual Entrepreneurs Conference
Atlanta, GA
(212) 242-8000
www.blackenterprise.com

May 18-20, 2010
Edison Electric Institute
Supplier Diversity Conference
Kansas City, MO
(202) 508-5000
www.eei.org

May 19, 2010
National Minority SupplierDevelopment Council
NMSDC Minority Business Leadership Awards Dinner-Dance
New York, NY
(212) 944-2430 ext 118
www.nmsdcus.org

May 19, 2010
Mid-American Minority Business Development Council
14th Annual Business Opportunity Fair
Overland Park, KS
(816) 221-4200
www.mambdc.org

May 19, 2010
Mid-American Minority Business Development Council
14th Annual Business Opportunity Fair
Overland Park, KS
(816) 221-4200
www.mambdc.org

May 20, 2010
Pittsburgh Regional Minority Purchasing Council
PRMPC Business Opportunity Fair
Pittsburgh, PA
(412) 391-4423
www.prmpc.org

May 24-26, 2010
South Central Ohio Minority Supplier Development Council
Business Opportunity Fair
Columbus, OH
(513) 579-3133
www.scomsdc.org

May 25-27, 2010
US Pan Asian American Chamber of Commerce
CelebrAsian 2010 Conference
Washington, DC
(202) 296-5221
www.uspaacc.com

May (TBD), 2010
US Small Business Administration
SBA Expo 2010
(Celebrating National Small Business Week)
Washington, DC
(202) 205-6474
www.sba.gov

May (TBD), 2010
Dallas/Fort Worth Minority Business Development Council
Access Expo 2010
Arlington, Tx
(241) 630-0747
www. dfwmbdc.com

May (TBD), 2010
St Louis Minority Business Council
Business Opportunity Fair & Construction Opportunity Summit
St. Louis, MO
(314) 241-1143
www.slmbc.org

JUNE 2010

June 9-11, 2010
National Association of Women Business Owners (NAWBO)
2010 Annual Women's Business Conference
Washington, DC
(800) 55-NAWBO
www.nawbo.org

June 10-12, 2010
Fraser Network
9th Annual PowerNetworking Conference
Atlanta , GA
(216) 691-6686
www.frasernet.com

June 13-16, 2010
Edison Electric Institute
2010 Annual Convention/Expo
Hollywood, FL
(202) 508-5131
www.eei.org

June 16-17, 2010
Kentuckiana Minority Supplier Development Council
Business Opportunity Fair
Louisville, KY
(502) 625-0147
www.kmbc.biz

June 19-22, 2010
Airport Minority Advisory Council (AMAC)
26th Annual Airport Business Diversity Conference
New Orleans, LA
(703) 417-2622
www.amac-org.com

June 22-24, 2010
Women's Business Enterprise National Council (WBENC)
11th Annual Women In Business National Conference & Business Fair
Baltimore, MD
(202) 872-5515 ext 8020
www.wbenc.org

June (TBD), 2010
New York / New Jersey Minority Supplier Development Council
Business Opportunity Expo
New York, NY
(212) 502-5663
www.nynjmsdc.org

June (TBD), 2010
Northwest Minority Business Council
Showcase 2010 Minority Business Conference & Opportunity Fair
Seattle, WA
(206) 575-7748
www.mmbc.biz/home

June (TBD), 2010
National Association of Minority Contractors (NAMC)
40th Annual National Conference
Charlotte, NC
(202) 347-8259
www.namcline.org

JULY 2010

July 10-13, 2010
National Council of La Raza
NCLR Annual Conference
Chicago, IL
(202) 785-1670
www.nclr.org

July 10-15, 2010
National Association for the Advancement of Colored People
100th Annual Convention
New York City, NY
(410) 580-5780
www.naacp.org

July 11-16, 2010
Amos Tuck School of Business Administration
Dartmouth College
Minority Business Executive Program
(Growing A Minority Business to Scale)
Hanover, NH
(603) 646-3740
www.tuck.dartmouth.edu

July 14-15, 2010
Oklahoma Minority Supplier Development Council
32nd Annual Business Conference and Opportunity Fair
Tulsa, OK
(405) 767-9900
www.omsdc.org

July 22, 2010
Latino Business Conexion
LA's Largest Mixer X
Los Angeles, CA
(323) 230-5656
www.largestmixer.com

July 26-31, 2010
National Urban League
2010 Annual National Conference
Washington, DC
(212) 558-5300
www.nul.org

July (TBD), 2010
Southern California Minority Business Council
Supplier of the Year Luncheon
Los Angeles, CA
(212) 689-6960
www.scmbdc.org

July (TBD), 2010
Grand Canyon Minority Supplier Development Council
Annual Business Opportunity Showcase & Trade Fair
Phoenix, AZ
(602) 495-9950
www.gcmsdc.org

July (TBD), 2010
Native American Business Alliance (NABA)
NABA Fund 9th Annual Business Conference
Choctaw, MS
(248) 988-9344
www.native-american-bus.org

AUGUST 2010

August 4-7, 2010
Florida Minority Supplier Development Council
27th Annual Conference and Trade Fair
Orlando, FL
(407) 245-6062
www.fmsdc.org

August 5, 2010
Northern California Supplier Development Council
NCSDC Annual Minority Business Opportunity Trade Fair
San Francisco, CA
(510) 686-2555
www.ncsdc.org

August 12-17, 2010
National Institute of Governmental Purchasing (NIGP)
65th Annual Forum
San Antonio, TX
(800) 367-6447 x227 or x242
www.nigp.org

August 18-19, 2010
Diversity Information Resources (DIR)
15th Annual "Best Practices" in Supplier Diversity Seminar
Chicago, IL
(612) 781-6819
www.diversityinforesources.com

August 18-20, 2010
California Black Chamber of Commerce
14th Anniversary Conference
Manhattan Beach, CA
(916) 463-0177
www.calbcc.org

August 25-26, 2010
Tennessee Minority Supplier Development Council
2010 Marketplace of Opportunities
Nashville, TN
(615) 259-4699
www.tmsdc.net

August 30- September 1, 2010
Minority Supplier Development Council of PA-NJ-DE
2010 Opportunity Convention
Atlantic City, NJ
(215) 569-1005
www.msdc-panjde.org

August (TBD), 2010
Carolinas Minority Supplier Development Council
32nd Annual Business Opportunity Conference
Charlotte, NC
(704) 549-1000
www.carolinasmsdc.org

August (TBD), 2010
Louisiana Minority Business Council
Business Opportunity Expo -Gateway 2010
New Orleans, LA
(504) 299-2960
www.lambc.org

August (TBD), 2010
US Department of Commerce-Minority Business Development Agency
National Conference
TBA
(202) 482-1617
www.mbda.gov

August (TBD), 2010
Arkansas/ Mississippi Minority Business Council
22nd Annual Business Opportunity Fair
Little Rock, AR
(501) 374-7026
www.ammbc.org

SEPTEMBER 2010

Semptember 1-4, 2010
National Association of Women in Construction
55th NAWIC Annual Convention
Louisville, KY
(817) 877-5551
www.nawic.org

September 7, 2010
Great Plains Minority Supplier Development Council
ACCESS 2010 Business Conference & Expo
Omaha, NE
(402) 614-9355
www.gpmsdc.com

September 12-14, 2010
WITI: Women In Technology International
Women In Technology Summit
Silicon Valley, CA
(818) 788-9484
www.witi.com

September 14, 2010
Great Plains Minority Supplier Development Council
Access Expo 2010
Omaha, NE
(402) 614-9355
www.gpmsdc.com

September 15, 2010
Congressional Hispanic Caucus Institute
33rd Annual Gala
Washington, DC
(202) 543-1771
www.chci.org

September 17, 2010
Asian Enterprise Magazine
17th Annual Asian Entrepreneur of the Year Awards
Los Angeles, CA
(909) 860-3316
www.asianenterprise.com

September 21-25, 2010
National Black MBA Association
32nd Annual Conference & Exposition
Los Angeles, CA
(312) 236-2622
www.nbmbaa.org

September 23, 2010
Midwest Minority Supplier Development Council
MMSDC Business Opportunity Fair
St Paul, MN
(612) 465-8881
www.mmsdc.org

September 24, 2010
Florida Regional Minority Business Council
34th Annual Awards Gala
Miami, FL
(305) 762-6151
www.frmbc.org

September 29- October 1, 2010
Greater New England Minority Supplier Development Council
Business Opportunity Expo
Ledyard, CT
(203) 288-9744
www.cmsdc.org

September 29- October 2, 2010
US Hispanic Chamber of Commerce
31st Annual Convention & Business Expo
Dallas. TX
(202) 842-1212 ext 497
www.ushcc.com

September (TBD), 2010
MEDWeek 2010
National Minority Enterprise Development Week Conference
Washington, DC
(888) 836-7647
www.medweek.gov

OCTOBER 2010

October 1, 2010
Oklahoma Minority Supplier Development Council
20th Annual Leadership Awards Dinner
Oklahoma City, OK
(405) 767-9900
www.omsdc.org

October 5, 2010
Michigan Minority Business Development Council
26th Annual Awards Dinner
Detroit, MI
(313) 873-3200
www.mmbdc.com

October 6-8, 2010
University of Wisconsin Executive Education School of Business
8th Annual Women's Executive Leadership Summit
Madison, WI
(608) 441-7330
www.exed.wisc.edu

October 6-7, 2010
Houston Minority Business Council
EXPO 2010- 34th Annual Business Opportunity Marketplace
Houston, TX
(713) 271-7805
www.hmbc.org

October 11-15, 2010
Business & Professional Women USA
78th National Business Women's Week
Washington, DC
(202) 293-1100
www.bpwusa.org

October 19, 2010
Tennessee Minority Supplier Council
18th Annual Minority Business Development Conference
Knoxville, TN
(615) 259-4699
www.tmsdc.net

October 21-22, 2010
Hispanic Women's Corporation
25th Annual HWC Conference
Phoenix, AZ
(602) 954-7995
www.hispanicwomen.org

October 24-27, 2010
National Minority Supplier Development Council (NMSDC)
NMSDC Annual Conference & Business Opportunity Fair
Phoenix, AZ
(212) 944-2430
www.nmsdc.org
www.nvmbc.org

October (TBD), 2010
Council Enterprises Inc.
AT&T Supplier Diversity Symposium
Milwaukee, WI
(608) 241-5858
www.suppliercouncil.org

NOVEMBER 2010

November 14-19, 2010
Amos Tuck School of Business Administration
Dartmouth College
Advanced Minority Business Executive Program
(Building a High Performing Minority Business)
Hanover, NH
(603) 646-3740
www.tuck.dartmouth.edu

November (TBD), 2010
Minority Business Council
16th Annual Minority Business Opportunity Expo & Trade Fair
Shreveport, LA
(318) 677-2500
www.shreveportchamber.org

DECEMBER 2010

December 3, 2010
Florida Regional Minority Business Council
2010 Minority Business Symposium
Pembroke Pines, FL
(305) 762-6151
www.frmbc.org

December 5, 2010
Central & South Texas Minority Business Council
Annual Awards Banquet
San Antonio, TX
(512) 386-8766
www.cstmbc.org

December (TBD), 2010
Mid-American Minority Business Development Council
Holiday Bash @ Boulevard Brewery
Location (TBD)
(816) 221-4200 ext 104
www.mambdc.org

December (TBD), 2010
Greater New England Minority Supplier Development Council
Annual Awards Dinner
Boston, MA
(617) 578-8900
www.nemsdc.org

SECTION 18

MINORITY & WOMEN PRESS

Listed are magazines and other publications which focus on the minority & women business community

Asian Enterprise Magazine
P O Box 2135
Walnut, CA 91788
(909) 860-3316
Fax (909) 860-7054
www.asianenterprise.com

Black Enterprise Magazine
130 Fifth Ave, 10th Fl
New York, NY 10011-4399
(212) 242-8000
www.blackenterprise.com

Catalyst Bookstore
120 Wall Street, 5th Fl
New York, NY 10005
(212) 514-7600
Fax (212) 514-8470
www.catalyst.org

Diversity Inc
Diversity Inc. Media
P O Box 32069
Newark, NJ 07102
(973) 494-0500
www.diversityinc.com

Enterprising Women Magazine
1135 Kildaire Farm Rd, Ste 200
Cary, NC 27511
(919) 362-1551
Fax (919) 362-9898
www.enterprisingwomen.com

Hispanic Business
425 Pine Ave
Santa Barbara, CA 93117-3709
(805) 964-4554
Fax (805) 964-5539
www.hispanicbusiness.com

Hispanic Network Magazine
6845 Indiana Ave, Ste 200
Riverside, CA. 92506
(800) 433-9675
Fax (951) 276-1700
www.hnmagazine.com

Hispanic Magazine
6355 Northwest 36th Street
Virginia Gardens, FL 33166
(305) 774-3550
Fax (305) 774-3578
www.hispanicmagazine.com

Journal of Asian Business
Center for International Business Education
U of M Business School
701 Tappan St
Ann Arbor, MI 48109-1234
(734) 936-3917
Fax (734) 936-1721
www.umich.edu/~cibe/faculty/jab.html

Latin Business Association (LBA)
120 S San Pedro St, Ste 530
Los Angeles, CA 90012
(213) 628-8510
Fax (213) 628-8519
www.lbausa.com

MBE (Minority Business Entrepreneur) Magazine
3528 Torrance Blvd., Ste 101
Torrance, CA 90503-4826
(310) 540-9398
Fax (310) 792-8263
www.mbemag.com

Minorities and Women in Business
3961 Clay Place NE
Washington, DC 20019
(866) 542-1387
Fax (202) 584-0387
www.mwib.com

Minorities in Business Insider
CD Publications
8204 Fenton St
Silver Spring, MD 20910-4517
(301) 588-6380 or (800) 666-6380
Fax (301) 588-6385
www.cdpublications.com

Minority Business News USA
TexCorp Communications, Inc
131111 N Central Expy, Ste 400
Dallas, TX 75243
(214) 369-3200 ext 29
www.mbnusa.biz

The Network Journal
Black Professional & Small Business Magazine
39 Broadway, Ste 2120
New York, NY 10006
(212) 962-3791
www.tnj.com

WE Women's Enterprise USA
13111N Central Expy, Ste 400
Dallas, TX 75243
(214) 369-3200 ext 29
www.weusa.biz

Index

N

O

P

P

Q

R

S

S

T

U

V

W